Hasso G. Stachow was born in 1924, was in the Hitler Youth from the age of nine, and was an NCO in an élite infantry unit in Russia, where he fought, despite several wounds, until the final defeat of Germany. A journalist since the war, he is today a high-ranking editor in a major German magazine syndicate.

HASSO G. STACHOW

If This Be Glory

*Translated from the German
Der Kleine Quast
by J. Maxwell Brownjohn*

GRANADA
London Toronto Sydney New York

Published by Granada Publishing Limited in 1983

ISBN 0 586 05775 7

A Granada Paperback UK Original
English translation copyright © Doubleday & Company,
Inc. 1982
German language edition entitled *Der Kleine Quast*
copyright © Droemersche Verlagsanstalt Th. Knaur Nachf
Gmbh & Co. 1979

Granada Publishing Limited
Frogmore, St Albans, Herts AL2 2NF
and
36 Golden Square, London W1R 4AH
515 Madison Avenue, New York, NY 10022, USA
117 York Street, Sydney, NSW 2000, Australia
60 International Blvd, Rexdale, Ontario, R9W 6J2, Canada
61 Beach Road, Auckland, New Zealand

Printed and bound in Great Britain by
Cox and Wyman Ltd, Reading
Set in Times

Herbert Quast told me this story in the course of twelve long interviews. Although persons and places have been renamed and dates altered, the events described here took place. Herr Quast has read the text and confirmed its accuracy.

H.G.S.

1

AUTHOR: *Would you say you'd been cheated out of your
youth?*

QUAST: *I was happy at first. I had time enough to
dream and not too many restrictions on my free-
dom. Isn't it a bit overdone, though, all this talk
about the happiest days of your life? There's so
much you've still to learn, so much you don't know
and can't do, so many things you're too young
for – and grown-ups can be so insensitive.*

*We took refuge in campfire romanticism, never
mind what emblem adorned the flags that flew
above our tents.*

Blue ink and red ink smelled different. The inkblot on the
school bench might have been a real live spider. You had
to make sure there was no fluff on your nib or the whole
page looked fuzzy. The copybook F wasn't a letter at
all – it was a lady in a long skirt with a bow around her
waist, and the M was a thread of smoke curling from a
chimney.

Karl-Günther was dipping little balls of blotting paper
in ink and flicking them at the wall with his penholder
while Blaschke's back was turned. They stuck there,
looking like bugs.

Elfriede's hand, with its dimpled knuckles, was shielding her dictation book so Eduard couldn't crib. Eduard,
who was a dunce, flushed with annoyance, because he
didn't know whether to spell Hanover with one *n* or two.

It was exciting, tracing letters on crisp white paper with

grey lines. It was like running barefoot across a sandy beach licked smooth by the waves. How far away they seemed, those blissful summer vacations beside the Baltic . . .

What was that last sentence – what had Blaschke just read out? He walked to the window and pretended to admire the view, then turned abruptly. Had he caught someone cribbing? No, no one. He began to polish his pince-nez with single-minded dedication.

Eduard nervously shuffled his feet. At once, the others followed suit. How restless they all were, and how sheepish they all looked! Hilde blew her nose with a sound like a trumpet. Outside, a dog was barking. A fly drummed against pane. Stupid thing – the window was open.

Blaschke dictated the final sentence, overstressing each syllable like one of the Party lecturers whose voices rattled the windows of the local inn on Saturday nights. His false teeth gave a decisive click. 'All right, ladies and gentlemen, shut your books. Rumprecht, collect them – carefully, now!'

The bell started ringing. They all streamed out of the classroom chattering, but not as light-heartedly as usual. The eight-year-olds congregated in the playground. Mean old Blaschke! He'd given them dictation without the customary one day's notice, just before their end-of-term reports were due. None of them had had a chance to brush up on spelling, and most of them, who were far from model pupils, could already feel the cuffings and canings that bad marks in German were bound to earn them.

Little Herbert Quast was standing on the fringe of the group. He had tousled fair hair and a permanent air of surprise. His thin chest was encased in a checked shirt, and his brown matchstick legs protruded from a pair of baggy shorts. His shoes, too, were on the large side, and his coarse woollen stockings were rolled down to the ankle, exposing a grubby plaster on one knee. He scuffed the sand with his toe cap and stared from face to face, eyes wide and eyebrows raised. Quast himself had nothing to fear. He enjoyed German lessons, because composition and dictation came easy to him. As for history, Blaschke's accounts of the Battle of Tannenberg in 1914 left him wishing that class would never end. His eyes shone, his cheeks turned pink with excitement, and the tide of battle was faithfully mirrored in his face.

Now, however, his childish features registered nothing but a mixture of dismay, indignation, and sympathy. Injustice had been done, and injustice – even when it didn't affect him personally – made little Quast see red. He drew his friend Karl aside. Karl had a bullet head, clean-shaven except for a swath of blond stubble along the hairline, a gap in his front teeth big enough to put his tongue through, and the scab of a recent graze on his pointed chin. He was chewing a blade of grass. Karl's green shirt was as baggy as Quast's pants. His cut-down grown-up's trousers, which were roughly hemmed, half concealed a pair of knobbly knees. The two boys were standing beside the wire-mesh fence that protected the janitor's red-currant and gooseberry bushes from school-boys' nimble fingers. In the background, beside a rain-water butt, sheets and towels were billowing on the clothes-line.

'We've got to get rid of those books,' Quast whispered.

Karl nodded. 'Blaschke put them in the cupboard. He won't go through them till tomorrow morning.'

'So it'll have to be this afternoon, right?'

'Right!'

Just before four, they scaled the tall fence separating the school premises from the outside world. Spikes surmounted the iron railings, and the brick columns were crenellated like the turrets of a fortress. They secreted themselves in the pine trees flanking the path that led to the main entrance of the austere red-and-black brick building. The janitor wasn't around, but they could hear his wife clattering dishes in the kitchen. The door was

9

open. They tiptoed upstairs. The banister rail had brass knobs every two feet to keep boys from sliding down. The floorboards were worn away, except where little hummocks surrounded the nails, securing them to the joists beneath. The air smelled strongly of timber steeped in linseed oil. On the landing stood an enamel spittoon filled with yellow sand.

The classroom at the far end of the green corridor was unlocked. The door creaked open. They paused to listen, but all they could hear was the distant clatter of cartwheels on cobblestones. The room was redolent of linseed oil, dust, chalk, ashes left in the clumsy cast-iron stove, and sweat. Quast glanced through the tall window. A haze hovered above the roofs of prosperous suburban homes framed by treetops – pines, alders, limes, and beeches. The wrought-iron curlicues and rosettes of the ornamental ironwork on the cupolas of their turrets and oriels, their elaborate weathercocks and weather vanes, were damascened into an afternoon sky of bluish pink. Not a leaf was stirring.

The door of the cupboard was secured with a simple padlock. The two boys tugged and wrenched until it gave with a sound like a pistol shot. They froze, holding their breath while the echoes died away, but nothing broke the silence outside. There was the pile of exercise books. Grab them and get going! They pushed the cupboard door shut and listened for footsteps in the corridor. Nothing. Now back down the stairs. They opened the door a crack. No sign of life on the path or in the street beyond. The janitor's wife was still washing up. Quast, with the exercise books under his arm, whispered, 'I'll go first so nobody sees us together.' He tiptoed along the path and shoved the books through the railings, then breasted the horizontal bar and got one foot between the uprights. Precariously poised above the spikes, he leaped for the sidewalk.

And there, only a few yards away, was Schaper. 'What

are you up to?' he asked suspiciously. Quast edged in front of the pile of books, but Schaper had already spotted them. 'Scram,' said Quast. 'It's none of your business. And keep your trap shut.' But Schaper's narrowed eyes and evil smirk conveyed that he had fathomed the situation.

Schaper was a gangling boy with chewed fingernails, pimply skin, pale grey red-rimmed eyes, a pointed nose forever laden with a dewdrop, and a chapped lower lip. In Quast's opinion, Schaper was sly, malicious, and untrustworthy. He had kicked Quast in the back of the knee during football and told tales on Karl. In disgust, Quast had called Schaper a skunk and been carpeted by Blaschke for his pains. They had fought each other, and Schaper had lost in spite of trying to use his teeth.

Karl, who was watching unseen from behind a tree trunk, winced with apprehension. He saw Quast advance on Schaper menacingly. Schaper scuttled off but stopped after a few yards and sauntered down the street with his hands in his pockets, whistling. He turned as he went and gave Quast a last malevolent look.

Schaper was bad at German. His dictation was bound to be rotten. Would he squeal or not? Would his hatred of Quast prevail, or would he count himself lucky to have escaped yet another bad mark?

The two friends crouched in a hollow in the sandy wasteland that stretched away to the horizon from the outskirts of their Berlin suburb – a desolation of timber yards, coal yards, warehouses, carpenter's workshops, forges, stables, and cow sheds. Pine trees glowed red in the setting sun, and a cool evening breeze stirred the clumps of arid grass that alternated with tracts of yellow, brown, and grey sand. The boys dug a pit with their bare hands, tore and crumpled up the exercise books. The flames subsided quickly. They poked at the ashes in silence. 'Keep your mouth shut tomorrow – you don't know a thing, understand?' said Quast. Karl nodded,

11

looking embarrassed. Schaper would be crazy to squeal, Quast had decided. What good would it do him?

Quast was in high spirits when he dashed into the classroom just before eight next morning. He turned pale with shock.

Blaschke was already there, and beside him stood Schaper – the champion of righteousness – with his flushed face set in an evil grin. The other pupils sat silent and spellbound. Blaschke's gold-rimmed pince-nez glinted on his bulbous nose. Quast made no attempt to deny the charge.

'But why you, Quast, when your marks in German are always so good?'

Quast said nothing. He scanned his schoolmates' faces. Their fear of getting a bad mark just before the end of term had been dispelled. Even if Blaschke gave them another dictation, he wouldn't catch them unawares. Now they had a spectacle to enjoy. Gleeful anticipation of another's punishment, self-righteous abhorrence of theft, contempt for someone stupid enough to get caught, heartfelt satisfaction at not being in his shoes – all these emotions were clearly discernible. Karl alone glared at Schaper, thirsting for revenge. As for Renate Hübner – the circus horse, as Quast had nicknamed her on account of her long flaxen ringlets and pink satin bows – her head was on one side and her protuberant blue eyes were misty with compassion.

Quast cursed himself for not putting on some thicker underpants, but he was already bending over. Blaschke tested the pliancy of his bamboo cane – 'Uncle Yellow,' he called it – and deliberately forced Quast's head down low over the edge of the ink-stained desk top. If Schaper had not been standing alongside, Quast would have given his tears free rein. The thin linen pants which his grandmother had made, though extolled in the family circle for their airy but durable qualities, afforded little protection against the bite of the cane. Blaschke hit him as hard as he could, determined to make an example of him. Quast gritted his teeth, but his eyes were watering by the time it was over. Tottering back to his place, he despairingly but consolingly reflected that the Battle of Langemarck had called for even greater powers of endurance.

One early-summer afternoon a year later, Herbert Quast had occasion to console himself once more with thoughts of Langemarck and Tannenberg, Douaumont and Annaberg. He could hardly feel his legs, and the blister on his left heel burned like fire. Why did the knapsack straps keep slipping off his shoulders? The pack was far too big for his nine-year-old frame, and the briquettes inside it chafed his skinny back. Hair stuck to his forehead and sweat seared his eyes. Never before had his lungs pumped so hard or his heart pounded so fiercely. The fine yellow-grey sand of the Märkische Heide grated between his teeth, and his mouth felt dry and furry. He was parched with thirst. Rudi, the dark, taciturn youngster who was trudging alongside in a khaki uniform, eyed him keenly. Did he sense that Quast had nothing left – that he'd lost the will to go on? But give up now? No, just ahead of them, where the track met a field of rye, lay the finish of their twelve-mile march.

So head up and chest out! Quast tried to smile, but all he produced was an agonized grimace. Another four steps, three, two, one: he was there!

Günther Hellwart, known as Heller, emerged from the pine trees. He gravely regarded the panting, swaying little boy through a pair of thick-lensed, nickel-framed glasses. Bristly inch-long hair stood up all over his quadrangular head.

'Congratulations, Herbert Quast, you made it. Now you're entitled to wear our uniform.'

They'd been after Quast ever since the affair of the stolen exercise books, which had exempted him from the usual test of courage. Now that he'd passed the endurance

13

test, Herbert Quast was a full-fledged member of the Protestant Youth Movement. He remained one for a few weeks only. Then he became a *Pimpf*, or junior member of the Hitler Youth: the Protestant Youth Movement had joined it *en bloc*.

Herbert Quast was nine years old when, in 1933, Germany succumbed to the raptures of National Socialism. He wore a black neckerchief gathered in a plaited leather ring, a brown, shirt, short black pants, and stout leather boots. From then on, his life was one long round of field exercises, evening get-togethers, sports days, leadership-training courses, and route marches.

It made his senses reel to hear how Germany had never been defeated in the field but treacherously stabbed in the back by homegrown Reds and fettered by the Versailles Treaty. His heart pounded at the thought that he and his comrades would one day band together to regain their country its rightful status in the eyes of the world.

Field and forest, meadow and stream, sun and rain – to a town-bred youngster like Quast, those things had so far been vague impressions casually gleaned on country walks with his elders. Now it excited him to meet the challenge of the elements, to feel the strength awakened in his limbs by hillside and moorland, to tramp across interminable fields of stubble and suppress the fears that haunted him during night patrols in the sinister gloom of dank and dripping forests. He also enjoyed wearing a real uniform instead of complying with the irksome dress regulations prescribed by school and family.

He was with his comrades one evening in a farmer's barn by the yellow light of hurricane lamps. The wind had dropped, and cattle were gently stirring in their stalls. Visible through the open door, the sun was submerging in a welter of cloud. The air smelled of hay, dung, wood-smoke, and the cocoa which, made with milk fresh from the udder, was steaming in a battered billycan. Piled on the shelter half beside it were doorsteps of fresh bread cut from a huge round loaf before their very eyes. The farmer's wife had baked it herself, and the sight of the dark brown crust, coupled with the nutty scent of farm-house butter, sent Quast into agonies of hunger. After supper came a singsong in which the boys were joined by farmhands gathered on the threshing floor. 'No finer land than ours we see, both far and wide, when seated 'neath the linden tree at eventide . . .' And when the damp night air struck chill, and they rolled themselves up in their blankets and snuggled deep into the hay, Quast's one remaining desire was that time would stand still for evermore.

But there were days of high adventure, too. Once, Quast was selected to capture the flag of the 'Chatti'. This Germanic tribal name had been adopted by a troop of about a hundred *Pimpfe* with whom his own troop, the 'Sugambri', had already competed on more than one field exercise. While Karl and two other boys sneaked up on the enemy camp in broad daylight and distracted the sentries' attention by collapsing a tent, Willi Schulze and Gerd Prüfer hurled themselves at the colour guard. Quast wrested the flag – a square of black bunting adorned with a white rune – from its custodian. Then he bundled it up beneath his arm and raced back into the woods, towing the unwieldy pole behind him. Before the defenders could collect their scattered wits, he had unscrewed the pole and was sprinting along the path to his own camp.

The Sugambri gave him an exultant welcome, but they didn't have long to savour their triumph. 'They're coming!' reported a lookout. 'They've come to get their flag back!'

Concealed behind a ridge in front of their tents, in a clearing enclosed by pine trees, Quast and his comrades hugged the ground and waited. The Chatti bore down like a brown and black wave. A bugle sounded the charge: 'Potato soup, potato soup, the whole day long potato soup. Soup – soup – soup!' With a hoarse cry, the Sugambri sprang to their feet. The two lines collided. Seconds later, they had disintegrated into knots of struggling figures. A small group of Chatti managed to break through, but the camp guard stopped them short of their objective. Quast held one boy by the ankles while Karl tried to pin his arms to the ground, but he was strong as an ox. Just then, another bugle call rang out: the cease-fire. They helped their adversary to his feet and congratulated him on putting up a good fight. Spitting out a mouthful of sand, he said they weren't bad themselves. The clearing looked like a battlefield. Some of the panting youngsters were sprawled on the ground, others doubled up, others clutching their heads, others hobbling painfully.

Half an hour later they were all sitting around in a big circle, friend and foe alike. In their midst, with aching limbs and shining eyes, sat Herbert Quast. Leaves rustled, birds sang, grass waved gently in the breeze, and two hundred youthful voices assailed the sky: 'Comrades, the trumpet sounds! Today it summons us to wander. Tomorrow's sun will shine on us in Russia or in Flanders . . .'

Political lectures were another matter. Quast found them tedious, because they made so little sense. Banks that lent money had to make a profit, after all, or bank clerks like Karl's father wouldn't get paid. And how had the Jews unanimously agreed to exploit the nations of the world? And why so much praise for British diplomats and their gambits on behalf of the Empire when they were characterized as double-dealing scoundrels a month or two later? Why were the Poles so detestable? Problems outnumbered solutions, but of one thing Quast remained convinced: The Führer knew all the right answers, even if his teachers didn't.

He remained sure even when he caught sight of some brown-shirted stormtroopers standing amid the shattered remains of the lingerie-store window on his way to school one morning. The word 'Jew' had been daubed in white

16

paint on its door. Groups of people were standing around, staring. Why did some of the loiterers look so pleased? There was no sign of the quiet old couple whom Quast had sometimes glimpsed through the window. What had they done? Whom could they have harmed? Why the revulsion on so many faces? At whom was it directed, the Brownshirts or the two old people? A plump matron said, 'If the Führer only knew . . .' Next, a man in a raincoat: 'Synagogues are burning all over the place, haven't you heard?' Then an old woman with a thick Berlin accent: 'What's the point of that?'

Quast would gladly have stopped to listen, but he was late for school. 'What's the point of that?' The words lingered in his ears. Still, he consoled himself, the Führer must know what the point was.

He made only one attempt to bypass his instructors and gain a first-hand picture. If the Communist Manifesto was such a mine of information about the Bolshevik arch-enemy, he inquired during a political guidance class, why couldn't he study it himself? This question earned him some cold, mistrustful looks from his comrades and displeased the youthful ideologists in charge. Didn't he have any faith in the Führer's vision of the world? they asked, and that reassured him. Being young, he willingly accepted that he still had much to learn. The older he became, the more ardently he yearned to prove his mettle.

Quast's warlike ambitions were intensified by the outbreak of hostilities. They persisted when he left the family's bomb-damaged apartment in the Berlin suburbs and moved east to a furnished room in Warthegau, the province on the German-Polish marches. But there were no short cuts to glory: before winning his spurs he would have to gain his diploma, and that was quite as tough a proposition here, in a provincial high school, as it would have been in Berlin, where his secondary school had been converted into a police barracks. Although he lived

17

entirely for the future, he was still required to show proficiency in French, mathematics, physics, and the rest.

So there he sat with Fatty Franz, boning up on his Latin comprehension. 'Caesar gave orders to demolish the bridges . . .'

Franz nodded. 'Smart fellow, old Caesar. You think he really had such a hard time beating Vercingetorix?'

Quast said, 'No idea. He had to put on a show for the Romans back home, of course. The tougher his enemies the more brilliant his victories.'

For reasons of space, Franz had put the little state-subsidized radio set on top of his wardrobe. 'Dream when you're feeling blue,' it was burbling. Franz said, 'I wish it could be like that with the Russians. First a state of suspense. The whole of Greater Germany holds its breath, and then – wham! – a stroke of military genius. But my father says our boys outside Moscow have walked into a trap.'

They both fell silent, gazing out at the backyards of squat provincial houses that were no longer occupied by Poles and ethnic Germans alone. Now, late in 1941, their denizens included Germans from the Reich itself, from the Baltic States and Volhynia, Bukovina and Bessarabia, Banat and Transylvania. The boys stared at the wood-piles, stared at the patterns etched on a stuccoed wall by rain from a fractured gutter. 'Remember how we kissed, that evening in the mist?' shrilled the radio.

Franz said ruminatively, 'A nice quiet fumble with Helga's tits, that's what I could use right now . . .'

And then the music was jammed by a Russian transmitter. 'The Führer is lying! You will never take Moscow! Central sector, three hundred and eighty-six tanks – destroyed! Three hundred and seven guns – destroyed! Eighty-seven thousand men – killed! In a single week! The Führer . . .' The harsh voice receded into a mush of static, then boomed out once more. 'The soil of Russia has room for you all – all!'

In slow motion, Quast put his pencil down.

'Hell,' groaned Franz. He switched off the radio and prodded Quast in the ribs. 'Come on, let's box.'

Boxing was one of the sports on the examination syllabus. Franz was ambitious. Being a poor boxer, he had badgered Quast into training with him. Though many pounds lighter, Quast was quick on his feet and an accurate puncher. They planned to meet in the test bout, and Quast had promised to make Franz look less sluggish than he really was.

A few minutes later they were both in gym clothes and facing each other across the hallway of the apartment, which had belonged to a Polish Army captain, present whereabouts unknown.

'Keep your guard up, Fatty!' Quast shouted. 'Try a right cross. Higher! Don't just stand there like a sack of potatoes, get those feet moving. Sidestep! You'll have to be quicker with Helga or you'll end up with an armful of nothing. And a left, and a right, one – two, one – two!'

Five minutes' sparring was enough. They stood there looking at each other – panting, shapeless twelve-ounce gloves hanging limp – but their eyes were alight with exhilaration.

Gudrun had turned up. Quast met her on the outskirts of the little town, where the road veered off through a cutting. It was cold, and the fields were thinly coated with snow.

A few days earlier, they'd rehearsed some Christmas carols with members of the tenth grade, over half of whom were girls. Beguiled by the music, Quast had dreamily allowed his eyes to wander. They came to rest on a dainty profile – a serene and serious face framed by long blond tresses.

'My mother made an awful fuss,' Gudrun said. 'Imagine going out in this weather, it'll be dark soon – nag, nag, nag!'

Her nose was cherry red and her lower lip stiff with cold. Quast knew that everything was against him – the time, the place, the weather, even Gudrun's idle chatter – but he simply had to be alone with her.

'Come on, let's walk a little.'

He tucked her arm into the crook of his elbow, but they were both so muffled up that all he could detect was a wad of clothing, not the nearness of her. The gesture seemed comic rather than romantic. They suddenly felt constrained and ill at ease. Quast didn't know how to start. I go for you? Obviously he did. Do you go for me? No need to ask. I'll go crazy if you don't let me kiss you this minute! He was crazy already.

He took Gudrun in his arms and kissed her, but his would-be display of masterful passion degenerated into a clumsy pass. Their eyes streamed in the biting wind. Although Gudrun returned his frost-bitten semblance of a kiss, she said, 'The wind's pretty nippy, isn't it? It's getting dark, too, and the road's so slippery.'

Quast nodded unhappily.

'Tomorrow evening,' she said, 'after choir practice. See me home – my parents won't be back till late.'

'Sure,' said Quast; then: 'Damn! I can't. Training.'

'All right, tomorrow afternoon. I'll be at Ursula's. Pick me up there.'

He looked agonized. 'No good, I'm on duty.'

She gave him a curious stare. 'So what *do* you want?'

'You, of course.'

'Meaning what, exactly?'

He shrugged.

'How about Sunday?'

Dejectedly, he said, 'I'm tied up. There's a gym match against the noncoms' training school.'

Gudrun said, 'You're crazy!' and turned on her heel. Without looking at him, she added, 'I want to go home.'

* * *

The town's main square was known as the Ring, or Rynek, as the Poles called it. Its centrepiece was the town hall, a stern two-storeyed building designed by Schinkel at a time when the province of Posen-West Prussia still existed, and bordering it were the narrow-fronted houses of the prosperous middle class. Other features of the Ring included the leading hotel, the Deutsches Haus, and the Old Pharmacy, with the words 'Stara Apteka' clearly visible beneath the German lettering on its repainted fascia. Down a side street that widened to form a triangular paved forecourt stood the Catholic church. Here, Catholic meant Polish.

The bleak, neo-Gothic red brick building was always packed. On the day when able-bodied Poles had been roused from their beds at 4 A.M. and herded into trucks for forced labour in the Reich, loudly lamented by their tearful families, the congregation had overflowed into the forecourt. Hundreds of grim-faced men and women listened to the sermon with a brooding intensity that masked the hatred seething within them.

These displays of steadfast patriotism were a particular thorn in the side of the local German minority, whose pent-up loathing of all things Polish was now running riot after years of suppression.

Quast was in a hurry that morning. He disliked being late for class, but all thoughts of school were banished, if only for a minute or two, by the scene that met his eyes in the Ring.

The Pole was an elderly man, probably a farmer. The coarse, faded brown suit was too big for him, like the peaked cap resting on his ears. Pale, sunken cheeks contrasted oddly with the reddish skin of his leathery neck, and his hands were gnarled and bony. He stumbled on the Ring's uneven sidewalk, then looked up and flinched. Coming in the opposite direction were two young stormtroopers with beefy red faces. They looked frighteningly robust and capable of violence as they

21

strutted along in step, swinging their arms well away from the body.

One of the Brownshirts strode up to the Pole and abruptly slapped his face, first backhanded, then with his open palm. 'That'll teach you to take your cap off when you see a German uniform! Polacks have to stand in the gutter when German servicemen go past.'

'I tripped,' the Pole said sullenly, ' – I didn't see.' He was trembling.

'Well, keep your eyes open, swine!'

The peasant's head jerked to and fro as the youth went to work again. His cap flew off, and he vainly tried to shield his face.

Quast's knees had turned to jelly. The old man didn't stand a chance. 'Hey,' he called, 'don't – don't hit him any more!'

The watching Brownshirt rounded on him. 'What's the matter, Polack-lover, want some too?' His companion also turned. Both men's eyes were incandescent with bloodlust. The Pole seized his chance and scuttled off, leaving his cap on the cobblestones.

Quast said, 'I, er – '

'Mind your business, twerp,' said the first man, and Quast went his way feeling bemused and ashamed – not only of the other two but of himself for being a coward.

'All right, Quast, tell us about the British Empire's strategic bottlenecks. Start with the Mediterranean.' By the time Herr Bimbach opened his geography class with this question, five minutes later, Quast had forgotten all about the old Pole.

It wasn't until the same evening, when relaxation set in after a training session in the gym, that the incident surfaced in his mind.

The boys swarmed into the changing room, pulled on their itchy woollen sweaters, and climbed into the pants they'd outgrown – high-tide pants, they called them. Then they headed for home or digs, blinking in the darkness, filling their lungs with cold night air, rejoicing at their escape from bellowed instructions, glaring lights, and the smell of sweat and linseed oil.

Quite suddenly, Quast recalled the heart-rending fear in the old Pole's eyes, the helpless way he'd stood there, the two young Brownshirts' swaggering movements, and the malicious delight on their faces.

'You know,' he said to Franz, 'we've always been taught that ordinary folk are decent and courageous.'

'Well?' said Franz.

Quast described what had happened. 'What beats me is, if ordinary folk are as decent as all that, how come they're so damned good at bullying their own kind?'

Both at a loss for an answer, they plodded along in silence until, cold and weary, they went their separate ways.

Quast had been filled with profound joy and solemn fervour by the outbreak of war – a war he firmly believed to have been instigated by Germany's hereditary foes in the West with the aid of Polish troublemakers and serpent-tongued Jewish plutocrats. Now the walls of his cramped little room were plastered with maps. Poland, France, England (showing aerial targets), Norway, Yugoslavia, Greece, Crete, North Africa. Finally, Russia. Lucky his map showed the Volga, he reflected. And the Caucasus. And the Caspian. If the Wehrmacht conquered much more territory, he'd soon be out of coloured pins. At seventeen, he had only one worry: would he get to the front in time? Would Germany attain her objective and become a world power without the assistance of Herbert Quast? What a depressing thought!

2

AUTHOR: *Didn't you find army life unbearably crude and uncivilized?*

QUAST: *No more so than life in general. All you can do is cultivate a style of your own.*

AUTHOR: *But weren't you too young to stand the strain?*

QUAST: *People are always too something when it comes to the pinch – too young, old, tired, stupid, sick – but who cares?*

The Kurfürstendamm still looked quite peaceful early in 1942. Uniforms of blue and field grey seemed to blend quite naturally into the Berlin street scene. If the women's faces were more preoccupied and the men's less nonchalent than formerly, Herbert Quast didn't notice. He'd turned eighteen a few days earlier – though he looked younger – and was bound for the recruiting centre with a high school diploma in his pocket. No pre-military stint in the Labour Corps for him. He was volunteering for the Army as an officer cadet in Frederick the Great's 'queen of weapons', the infantry.

His goal was a corner building at the point where Grolmannstrasse and Uhlandstrasse joined the Kurfürstendamm. The grey concrete staircase struck a chill and impersonal note. A few clerks came strutting along the corridor, one with an empty sleeve. Rectangles of cardboard were thumbtacked to the doors: A–K inclusive, L–R inclusive, S–Z inclusive. Quast knocked, entered, saluted smartly.

'Heil Hitler, Sergeant Major, my name is Herbert Quast, I've come to volunteer. I – '

From across the counter, he was met by an amused glance from a grey-haired man in a crumpled uniform. 'Slow down, son. What was your name again?'

Five minutes later he was back outside on the landing. He had a week in which to submit various documents: his certificate of Aryan descent, papers relating to his father, his mother, testimonials from the Hitler Youth, his school, and so on. The sergeant major was being deliberately obstructive, he told himself – the very word 'submit' annoyed him beyond measure. How could he possibly produce the documents within a week? His father was doing civilian war work in Brno, or Königsberg, or somewhere – God alone knew. His mother was in Poznań, his sister somewhere in the West, his teacher in Warthegau. It was ages since the family's boarded-up apartment in Berlin had been more than a place to camp.

Quast didn't manage it. When he turned up a week later and deposited his meagre haul on the sergeant major's desk, the man's grin told him at once that he'd known the outcome all along. Quast protested. He politely asked for an exception to be made, but in vain. His dream of becoming an officer was over before it had begun.

'All right, sonny, stop yakking. I've made out your papers for Potsdam. Sign here.'

Quast hesitated.

'Look, they've been cutting down on cadet acceptances lately – and besides, you can always try for a commission later. You've got brains and you can talk straight, which makes you perfect Signal Corps material. I'm posting you to Potsdam. That means you can go home weekends, so you won't have to scrub your shirt collar with a toothbrush in barracks. You'll be grateful to me by the time you're through. Now sign here.'

'Yes, Sergeant Major.'

Quast ground his teeth but raised no further objection –

he was far too disconcerted for that. He'd always thought himself a genuine German, which to him meant a scion of the Nordic and Germanic race, but his dip into the family archives had turned up something untoward: there was Russian and Polish blood in his veins as well as Palatinate and Swedish. That made him a mongrel, and his pale blond hair, which was only gradually darkening, might well be a sign of Slavic descent, not Germanic.

Quast was relieved when the sergeant major showed absolutely no interest in his family records. He decided to stow them safely away and mention them to no one, and years were to pass before he learned to distinguish between race and character. Deftly gathering his documents together, he delivered a smart salute, which left the grizzled noncom unimpressed. His only response was 'All right, carry on.'

This elderly reservist with the wrinkled face, brown teeth, and ill-fitting uniform was among those who wanted Quast to survive the war. But Quast, as he sullenly and apathetically descended the stairs, could not be expected to know that.

The cold and musty climate of the barrack room held no terrors for Quast. He knew it well, having done a few weeks' pre-military training with the 67th Infantry at Spandau as a fifteen-year-old squad commander in the Hitler Youth. He had learned to define terrain ('I am situated in an area of broken ground.') He had also learned to shoot. ('The rifleman lies with his body straight but oblique to the target.) He had commanded an assault group during a field exercise and been schooled in the basics of Prussian military thinking ('I shall try to reach the white house left of the bushy-topped tree.' – 'Wrong! The correct form of words is, "I *shall* reach . . ."' – 'Yes, Sergeant!') Even so, he felt slightly apprehensive. His time as a real soldier had just begun.

There they stood in the barrack square, forty young

men carrying suitcases and cardboard boxes, and all with their shirt collars open. They had only just trudged through the gates in threes when the guard commander yelled, 'Ties off! You can put 'em on again when we've won the war.'

Then he was sitting in the radio room with twenty others of his kind. Before him lay a pencil, a pad, and a pair of earphones. The bored-looking sergeant at the Morse key said, 'Did-da is Anton, da-did-did-did is Berta, da-did-da-did is Caesar, got that? I repeat: Did-da, da-did-did-did, da-did-da-did. All right, put your headsets on. I'll send, you take it down.'

Quast donned his headset. There was a sudden cheeping sound, but its meaning eluded him. Where the hell did one Morse character end and the next begin? The pad in front of him bore his rank and name, 'Signaller Quast.' Otherwise, it remained blank.

Ten minutes later Quast learned that he was not radio-operator material. He was going to be a field telephonist instead. Off he went to No 3 Company, next door. Red brick buildings, a cindered parade ground, a barrack room with triple tiers of bunks. Through the window, a view of the Bornstedter Feld.

'That's where old Frederick's grenadiers used to sweat it out, and that's where you're going to do the same. There'll be steam coming out of your asses by the time I'm through with you, believe me!'

These words promptly defined the relationship between the squad commander, a waspish corporal with horn-rimmed glasses, and his cowed recruits.

One day they had to tote their lockers out on to the barrack square, because the orderly sergeant had discovered some specks of dust on a shelf. Some of them were indignant and a few sobbed with exhaustion and impotent rage. Quast laughed. He didn't know which amused him more, the instructors' ingenious methods of harassment or their bovine, self-important expressions.

On another occasion, long after lights out at 10 P.M., the recruits were roused from their bunks and paraded in the corridor in dress uniform because a bread crumb had been found by a table leg. When they were finally drawn up in single file on the worn and echoing flagstones, it was discovered that one of them had failed to bring his pocket comb. They were ordered into full field equipment and told to fall in in the square five minutes later. Each locker was shared by two men, so the instructors snickered with glee as their charges struggled to find the right steel helmet and pair of boots in the resulting confusion. Doubling back into the barrack room half an hour later, bathed in sweat, they found their lockers upended. The corporal, who was standing in the doorway grinning, declared that men who left their quarters like a pigsty must learn to be tidy the hard way. Dog-tired, with the breath rasping in their throats and their knees trembling, they cleared up the mess. They now knew what the regulars meant by a 'fancy-dress ball'. It was 1 A.M. Four hours to reveille.

The same thing happened morning after morning: as soon as the whistle sounded in the corridor, they all rolled out of their bunks and on to the barrack-room floor, no matter how fast asleep they'd been or whether they occupied the topmost of the three tiers. Almost simultaneously, the door burst open. Legs splayed, arms akimbo, and head jutting avidly, the corporal stood in the entrance. Anyone still in bed had his name taken – weekend fire duty, no pass into town – even before the duty signaller rapped out his report: 'Room Twelve, fifteen men. All up and fit for duty. Room orderly, Signaller Lawnitzak!'

No wonder they fell out of their bunks like bedbugs dropping off the barrack-room ceiling.

All of them were hollow-eyed from lack of sleep. Some dozed off as soon as they filed into the lecture room – after calisthenics and muster – to watch Russian training films on close combat and camouflage. None of them was wide awake enough to inquire why the world's finest army should be dependent on films that had, after all, been made by what Goebbels's propagandists referred to as subhuman scum from the East. Nobody concentrated on the tips that might one day make the difference between death and survival. They battled with sleep and learned nothing.

Quast felt sorry whenever one of their number collapsed in the heat while drilling. He thought it nonsensical to overtax soldiers before they'd seen anything of war, but he accepted his lot. The instructors, he found not only uncouth but inhuman. When the day's timetable opened with an hour of drill, and when the recruits thundered out on to the square in their hobnailed boots, queasy stomachs full of coarse cookhouse bread, burned-tasting jam, and watery coffee, many of them felt weak at the knees with foreboding at the torments that lay ahead. The instructors gathered on the right of the company, which was drawn up at ease on the square. From under the rim of his steel helmet, many a recruit glanced furtively at the fearsome beings assembled there with such lordly arrogance, smirking and leering as they recounted what they had done to their girl friends the night before. To the youngsters, they seemed like rapists. Having just bullied their womenfolk into submission, they were about to lay their subordinates low with the same brutal gusto. Put one man at the mercy of another, thought Quast, and Satan reared his head at once.

So it was with Sergeant Major Schack, an NCO instructor who had spent the past fifteen years living in, and for, the barracks. No sooner had they slumped on to the lecture room's tip-up seats, and no sooner had the first few feet of film been run, than Schack came padding silently along the rows under cover of darkness, crouching low. 'Name?' he would hiss if he caught a recruit with his eyes shut; then: 'Fire duty, Saturday and Sunday.' Schack prided himself on his technique. It always bore fruit, even with Quast. Sergeant Major Asshole, thought Quast, resolutely smiling as he watched Schack lick a pencil stub and take his name in a species of cuneiform. He could have sworn his eyes were open, but Schack had been determined to nail the young pup who invariably laughed instead of quaking with the awe-inspired respect due to a veteran noncom of his seniority.

Fire duty. The fire-fighting details for the entire barracks, a hundred or so strong, were drawn up in an open-ended square. The red brick blocks around them, which were strangely deserted and forlorn, had the bizarre ugliness of factories on vacation or railroad platforms when the rear lights of the last train have vanished into the distance. Facing the parade stood the orderly officer and his duty NCOs. A corporal was explaining the use of fire-fighting equipment in a bored monotone. The men's faces were blank. None of them even bothered to feign attention. No tramp of feet broke the all-pervading hush, no clatter of rifle butts, no words of command, no rumble of wheels: a weekend in barracks.

Quast preserved a loose-limbed stance, each leg ready to obey orders with the minimum of effort. Suddenly he stiffened. In the opposite rank, only ten yards away, was a pale face. It was – yes, it was Eberhard, a classmate from Berlin. Quast winked at him. Eberhard winked back. Quast made a covert signal. Eberhard nodded. At long last: 'Fall out!'

Eberhard didn't say, 'Hi!' or 'Quast!' as he wearily shook Quast's hand. He said, 'I'm going to kill myself.' He said it quite simply, not despairingly or melodramatically. Just, 'I'm going to kill myself.'

'Hey, Eberhard, what's the matter?'

'I can't take any more of it.'

'Any more of what?'

They stood there facing each other in their new green denim jackets with the cheap shine on them, field service caps squashed down on their heads and baggy trousers drooping over worn and misshapen boots. The barrack square had emptied by this time, leaving them lost in its vast expanse.

Eberhard stifled a sob. 'It's the hazing – I can't take it.'

'It'll soon be over. Only a few more weeks.'

'I'll be insane by then. That man Grotzke makes me crawl whenever he sees me. "Ah," he says, "it's our college boy again. If you're so goddamned smart, show us how to clean the recruits' latrine."'

'Dumb bastard, he can't get over being put in charge of people – it's gone to his head. Don't let it bother you.'

'It's all right for you. The swine keeps rummaging in my locker. When I see him mauling my books with his dirty great paws – '

'But that won't kill you, for God's sake!'

'Yes, it will. I only have to stretch out on my bunk and he's off: "Me, I come from a working-class family. I was hauling bricks when your mother was still wiping shit off your ass . . ." You can't imagine what it's like, Herbert.'

'Grotzke doesn't know any better. Think of growing up in some tenement that never sees the sun. Father out of work, mother worn to a frazzle, two or three kids in the same bed – and the stench! Nothing but dry bread and a clip on the ear for breakfast, and if you're naturally mean-minded to start with, like Grotzke – '

'Why should I care about his lousy childhood? He's a corporal now, and he wants to break me – *and* he's succeeded.' Eberhard's shoulders shook. 'I'm going to do him a favour. I'm going to hang myself from a pipe in the recruits' latrine, his favourite place, and I'll use these god-awful army suspenders. That ought to suit his proletarian taste.'

'You're joking.'

'No, Herbert, I mean it.'

Quast felt a pang of alarm. He studied the limp, pallid

face, the twitching mouth, the lacklustre eyes, the trembling hands. Eberhard was really at the end of his rope.

'Now listen, Eberhard. You know how we always admired you in class. You were great – always so calm and unflappable, never flustered. You can't do a bully like Grotzke the favour of hanging yourself – it isn't your style. Are you really planning to take your own life on account of a creature like that? You really want to breathe your last in a stench of ammonia and creosote and shit?'

Something dawned in Eberhard's eyes. Quast drew a deep breath and put his arm round Eberhard's shoulders. Eberhard wiped his eyes and gave a wry smile. If he looked at him much longer, thought Quast, he'd be blubbering himself.

'You know,' Eberhard said softly, 'I'd always thought the Army would be different . . .'

A few days later Quast caught sight of his German teacher, Herr Urban, dressed in faded grey denims. The jacket was too tight, the sleeves were too short, the pants too baggy, the over-sized cap sat perched on the back of his head. Though short and rotund, Urban had been a well-groomed man with polished fingernails and a fondness for dark three-piece suits. He spoke very rapidly, very wittily – sarcastically too, sometimes, when his pupils' stupidity became too much for him. His manner had been lofty and self-assured. Now he was lining up outside the cookhouse with a mess of trampled potato beneath his feet and a tin bowl in his shrunken red fist, staring glumly at the wall. Quast refrained from speaking to him. He didn't want to hurt the man.

At some stage during those weeks, which passed in an endless succession of muster rolls, drills, field training exercises, and technical instruction classes – at some stage during those weeks which became such a blur in his memory – Quast was sent for by the company commander, a thickset man with a fleshy, perspiring face. He was seated at a small table in his cell-like room. In one corner stood a camp bed with a coarse, drab grey blanket folded over the foot.

'Quast, I've put you down for the ROC course. You're a high school graduate, and we're short of officers.'

'I don't know, Lieutenant. I've only got a few more weeks to go – '

The lieutenant grunted impatiently. 'Report to the sergeant major and get your marching orders. You're joining the course tonight, and no arguments.'

Reserve Officer Cadet . . . The idea had suddenly lost its appeal. Quast wanted to see some action, not go on a course – not do another spell in barracks. Besides, there was a letter from his grandfather in his locker – a response to the news that he had joined the Army as a common signaller, not an officer cadet. Grandfather had been a captain in the Royal Prussian Army. 'Never mind,' he'd written, 'war's no picnic. First make sure that military service suits you.' Discounting the fact that the old gentleman who now counselled caution had often regaled his grandson with stirring accounts of World War I battles in which combat troops figured as radiant heroes and their officers as the most radiant heroes of all, he probably had a point. Quast had no time to dwell on the question as he plodded along the corridors of the administration building with his papers in his hand. Clothing store, armoury, quartermaster's office, orderly room – all these hurdles had to be cleared before he was free to leave.

That evening, he was back in barracks – modern ones, this time. The awesomely institutional character of the old red brick buildings had been redeemed by their turn-of-the-century patina. The new ones were oppressively dull. To Quast, their homely gabled roofs and unpretentious portals seemed vulgarly ingratiating.

He nursed a glamorized and enthusiastic vision of the challenge awaiting him. He had been taught that being an officer meant setting an example, excelling at everything,

33

valuing performance above outward appearance. His mind was still haunted by the martial maxims that had so deeply impressed him at the age of ten, when he had at last become entitled to wear the black neckerchief. 'Jungvolk boys are tough, tight-lipped, and true. Jungvolk boys are comrades. To the Jungvolk boy, honour is supreme.'

Here, however, these sentiments were out of place. Here everything reeked of self-interest and careerism. Here everyone was tough and tight-lipped towards others and true to his own ambitions. Comradeship? The word was greeted with disfavour.

Quast was the youngest in his platoon. He felt like a child among adults and had no comprehension of a world where everyone adopted such an aloof and hostile manner. All the other ROCs were older – twenty-three, twenty-five – and some had already seen action. They formed a separate, peculiarly self-contained group.

Their conversations meant nothing to Quast. What was it based on, all their arrogance and inflexibility? In his youthful enthusiasm, Quast was receptive, inquisitive, and eager to learn, but the others perplexed him with their cut-and-dried opinions. They played at being an élite but weren't one, he decided. As for their talk of women – of getting them drunk, stripping them, screwing them – his inexperience was such that he felt shocked and revolted by it.

Even his duties made no sense to him. What was the point of drilling for hours on end? Why weren't they taught how to command a body of men under varying conditions? What was combat really like?

But training had its brighter side, too. Quast could march: he successfully completed the thirty-mile route march in combat equipment, even though he spent part of it toting an MG34 machine gun. Quast could shoot: it fascinated him when he flexed his forefinger and a hole appeared like magic in the helmet of a dummy a hundred yards away. Yes, handling weapons was fun. Bayonets locked onto their mountings with a satisfying click, and rounds slid smoothly into the chamber. 'Cover me while I cross that gap! Eyes peeled, head up, finger off the trigger, disengage quietly. Crawl and glide. Chestnut Exchange here: Are you still talking, are you still talking? Disconnecting you now! The FK16 field telephone switchboard is so called because it was introduced into the German Army in 1916 . . .' All these things were logical, useful, and imbued with purpose.

Quast felt he was living in a world where even surprises formed part of a master plan, a world in which all was as it should be.

3

AUTHOR: *It almost sounds as if the Army wasn't Prussian enough for you in those days.*

QUAST: *True. I thought sensible orders and regulations were the key to correct action. It hadn't dawned on me that speech is an imperfect means of communication and that rank is no measure of a man's natural decency or concern for his subordinates.*

Drill was cut short one drizzly morning early that winter.

'Reports to Lieutenant Ellberg one at a time.'

Quast's turn came at last. A lecture room, its long rows of benches deserted. Rolf Ellberg, first lieutenant and Party member, was seated on a desk top in the front row. One of his legs, sheathed in an immaculately polished riding boot, was swinging idly. Beside his cap, with doeskin gloves inside, was a clipboard. Secured to the latter in alphabetical order were preprinted forms relating to each trainee, complete with photograph, personal particulars, and symbols whose meaning eluded Quast. He looked at the tall, wiry, inscrutable man with the angular head and lipless mouth, cold blue eyes and thin fair hair.

'You,' said Ellberg, and it sounded like a flourish of trumpets, 'are a bad soldier.' Outside, a column of trucks roared past. 'And that's a waste, because you could be a damned good one.' The drivers of the last two trucks down-shifted with a whine of gears. 'Well, why aren't you?'

Quast didn't answer. What was he meant to say? He

stood at attention, chin tucked in and thumbs aligned with trouser seams. Eventually, he said, 'I do what I'm ordered to, Lieutenant.'

'I know, but that's all. It shows.' Ellberg looked out the window, then back again. 'At ease, Quast.' Muffled by intervening barrack buildings, the roar of engines faded. 'You want to become an officer?'

'No, Lieutenant.'

'No? I must be going deaf. Did you say no?'

'No, Lieutenant, not this way.'

'Not which way? You'd better explain yourself.'

Ellberg sounded amiable enough. Gratified that such an influential man should be interested in his ideas, Quast took the plunge. 'Let's assume I make the grade, Lieutenant.'

'Very well, let's assume so.'

'If I do, I'll be sent to the front on eight weeks' probation. But say I don't end up in the front line proper – say I'm attached to a regimental exchange in a quiet sector. The noncoms have no intention of letting a would-be officer get in their hair. Some heavy shells come over and a couple of lines go phut. "Troubleshooters out!" I yell, but one of the noncoms tells me not to worry, the repair's already in hand. I realize then, if I didn't before, that they know a whole lot more than I do. Meantime, there's the regimental commander. I've whipped out my lighter and lit his cigarette a few times in the mess dugout, and I've always answered him loud and clear. When my eight weeks are up, he sends me home with a first-class assessment. The switchboard functioned like clockwork and I've definitely got the makings of an officer – or so it says in my personal file.'

Ellberg was sitting quite still, his face expressionless.

Quast, who had warmed to his subject, pressed on. 'Then I go to Signals School. Being reasonably bright, I make the grade. I get what everyone on this course is so keen to get: a brand-new pair of second lieutenant's shoulder straps. Hurrah, I say to myself, all the girls are panting for me, all my juniors will have to salute me from now on. We parade in the square of the Signals School – fifty young officers fresh from the egg. Two names are read out. Right face: off you go to the Signal Corps. The other forty-eight are assigned to the infantry.' Quast paused for breath.

Ellberg sat there as motionless as ever.

'Two weeks later, Lieutenant, I'm somewhere on the Eastern Front. My company is down to thirty men. The Russians are coming. My men are looking at me. They're waiting for orders, Lieutenant, but I don't know what to tell them, because I've never been taught. I know my circuit diagrams by heart, but I'm not authorized to open up a defective field telephone, whose guts I know like the back of my hand, nor a Mark B radio, nor a C, nor a D. I'm damn good at carrier-frequency telephony and permanent ways and jamming procedure, but I've only thrown one hand grenade in my life and never fired a zero-eight in anger. I've never learned about digging in or camouflage. After all, I'm supposed to become a Signals officer, though it's doubtful if I ever will, because nearly every officer's needed in the infantry. All I know for sure is, I haven't learned here what I'd need to know out there.' Quast was breathing fast now. Only while he was speaking had the sheer folly of his present training become wholly apparent.

Very deliberate, Ellberg rose and walked up to him. 'I see,' he said in a low, menacing voice. 'No doubt you've discussed this with your comrades, Quast?'

'No, Lieutenant, I've merely listened to them talking. My comrades are all preoccupied with themselves.'

'Unlike you. You see things in broad perspective, eh?'

'Only within the limits of what I know, Lieutenant.'

'Oh, yes, and what precisely *do* you know?' Ellberg put his hands on his hips. 'I'll tell you something for free, Quast: It's defeatism, what you said just now. We're turning out cannon fodder; that's the implication. You're undermining the morale of my course – *my* course! You're a disruptive influence – a rotten little subversive!'

Ellberg strode down the central aisle, almost bouncing with suppressed fury. Drill had resumed outside. 'Left face, right face, about face . . . Wait for it! Squad . . . halt! Stand still there!' Ellberg walked up to the blackboard, which bore the half-erased tactical sign for a horse-drawn signal platoon. Then he turned and advanced on Quast like an ogre in seven-league boots.

'You think too much,' he said, speaking softly at first but steadily turning up the volume. 'The Führer's wrong, the generals are wrong, the Army's wrong. Only Signaller Quast knows the score – that's what you think, isn't it? Very well, we'll have to make sure you don't get *time* to think. You're going to be up to your neck in shit from now on, and that's a promise!'

Quast realized that Lieutenant Ellberg had developed a sudden hatred for him. He'd bawled him out and threatened him, but he hadn't refuted his argument. Feeling apprehensive, Quast withdrew, resolved to be doubly on his guard.

The slave driver of the course was Master Sergeant Bendack, a sturdy, bull-necked man with huge hands and a perpetual grin. Although the furrows in his fleshy forehead were not indicative of any great intellectual activity, he was responsible to Lieutenant Ellberg for maintaining discipline and good order among the trainees. If Ellberg casually mentioned that one of the latter – in this case, Signaller Quast – was a slack and unsoldierly individual, Bendack had enough perspicacity to know which way the wind was blowing.

By the time Quast had been singled out on parade three times in succession, he knew it too. No matter how brightly he shined his boots, Bendack found them dull. No matter how carefully he sponged and pressed his uniform, Bendack found it creased and filthy.

It wasn't so easy on the rifle range. Quast habitually scored thirty to thirty-three points out of a possible thirty-six, which not even Bendack, with the worst will in the world, could take exception to. The same went for drills and practices. When filters were inspected during a gas alert, Quast's would be screwed in tight – to Bendack's chagrin. He kept on hoping to find Quast guilty of using illicit aids to respiration – a loose filter or a matchstick in the valve – but in vain. When the trainees had to 'duckstep' across the parade ground with their rifles at full stretch, Quast was never among the ten laggards who had to go through the whole performance again. But Bendack knew what was expected of him. Having finally discovered that when he gave the order, 'On your feet! Double march! Hit the dirt!' Quast didn't roll over properly, he chivied him around the square for forty-five solid minutes.

But even that failed to break the boy. Despite himself, Bendack developed a secret fondness for the little signaller. Quast's rifle drill and foot drill were flawless, his responses crisp and snappy. Bendack was honest enough with himself to admire how obediently Quast flung himself to the cinder surface of the parade ground, how exemplarily he rolled over on to his left knee while cradling his rifle like a sick baby. A lad after my own heart, he thought, and the tide of his sadistic whims ebbed. In the end, because Ellberg still wanted to see Quast suffer, he instructed him to stand with his back to the perimeter wall and shout, from a distance of a hundred and fifty yards, 'I'm a soldier, I like being a soldier, the Führer was lucky to get me!' Quast yelled like mad while Bendack feigned deafness with his head cocked and his mouth open. 'Did you say something? I didn't hear a thing!' And Quast went on yelling, and Bendack, with a doltish expression, cupped a big red hand to his ear.

So Quast learned a new lesson every day. He had taken

Ellberg literally when asked to explain himself. He now knew that he must never tell a superior what he thought, even when ordered to, but confine himself to what the superior wanted to hear. He was almost invariably crimson-faced and perspiring. His knees and elbows were grazed, his voice was hoarse, his glasses sat askew on his nose, and he had acquired a limp, but he strove to see things in a good light. Ellberg might think him a rotten little subversive, but no one was going to accuse him of being a slacker. Besides, he guessed that Bendack was easing up on him.

And Quast, the loner, had made some friends at last. A couple of fellow cadets helped him to darn his uniform, clean his rifle, polish his boots. Something akin to comradeship had, after all, declared itself among them. They were determined to see that Quast made the grade, but they had reckoned without Ellberg.

Two weeks later, some young Signal Corps recruits were to complete their basic training with a seven-day field exercise. Ellberg's officer cadets were assigned to various hot spots to show how much they, too, had learned. Quast, who had been given command of a signal detachment, felt uneasy from the moment the equipment was issued. The handcarts were rickety, there weren't enough telephones, and everything was worn and battered. To make matters worse, he was given an operational deadline that couldn't have been met even if his detachment had hauled the heavy handcarts for miles at a trot. They marched through the night and were late in reaching the place where they had been instructed to set up a divisional exchange. An umpire proceeded to complicate the issue by announcing that enemy troops had infiltrated the outskirts of the wood and Division was urgently in need of a telephone link.

Keep calm, Quast told himself. First, detail two men with a light machine gun to watch the wood and eliminate the risk of a surprise attack. Then dig a foxhole for the switchboard – no, put it on a tree stump and get a man to dig alongside. Telephone communication could be established and the switchboard lowered into the foxhole later, when it was deep enough. At that moment, a gaggle of pioneers burst from the undergrowth, wound some cables round the nearest tree, and jammed slips of paper under the loops to prevent confusion. '2nd Battalion cable!' they yelled. 'No 3 Battery cable! No 1, No 2 . . .' In an instant, Quast's men had set up the terminal box on which every cable was deftly arranged and identified before being connected to the switchboard.

That was when Quast caught sight of Lieutenant Ellberg approaching with the director of operations, a short, spruce, straight-backed colonel. A fire-eater – you could tell that a mile off. All Quast saw of him at first was a huge fur collar, and in it, beneath a cap worn at a jaunty angle, a lean, vulturine face with a beaky nose. Quast was also struck by his high-booted cavalryman's legs, the riding crop in his bony, freckled hand, and the clasp adorning his World War I Iron Cross. Ellberg leaned towards him and nodded in Quast's direction. The colonel abruptly raised his head and frowned. After that, everything happened very fast.

'Who's in command of this exchange?' The colonel fired this harsh-voiced inquiry from a range of twenty yards.

'I am, Colonel.' Quast stepped forward, saluted, and was scrutinized with icy detachment.

'Why hasn't that switchboard been dug in?'

'Division needs a telephone link badly, Colonel. I thought it more important to establish communication first.'

'You did, did you? Are you out of your mind?'

'No, Colonel. I'm getting good reception on all lines.'

'Don't be impertinent. Where's your test kit?'

'We don't have one, Colonel. I assume it's at the front.'

42

'So you assume that, do you? In that case, how do you check reception?'

'I disconnect the line and check with my operator's phone.'

'You do what? Good God, man, what happens if somebody calls?'

'I do a quick switch, Colonel. Beg permission to explain how the system works. This is the A Leg and this is the B Leg. If I take the cable and – '

The colonel emitted a guttural sound and angrily thrust his chin from its ruff of fur. 'So now you're teaching me electro-technology!' The riding crop stabbed the air at something beyond Quast. 'What are those bits of paper on the terminal box? Haven't you been taught to identify every line with a bone tag stating its destination?'

'Yes, Colonel, that's what we've been taught, but maybe the Army's run out of bone – tags, I mean. They're probably needed for the real thing.'

The colonel's voice shook and his face became suffused. 'This exchange is a shambles!'

'Yes, Colonel, a shambles.'

'Hold your tongue! Anyway, why are you undermanned?'

An embarrassed umpire stepped forward and started to explain the situation. 'Enemy patrols are infiltrating from the left, Colonel. Two men and an MG – '

Impatiently, the colonel brushed this aside. Nothing could be allowed to interrupt his frenzy. 'The hell with that!' He turned back to Quast. 'As for you, I'm giving you short shrift. You'll be transferred out on disciplinary grounds, for gross inefficiency and refractory conduct towards a superior officer.'

From behind the colonel, Ellberg glared at Quast with his eyes narrowed and the corners of his mouth turned down. But Hawknose wasn't through yet. His voice rose to a shout.

'You're going to Russia, my friend!'

'Any time, Colonel,' Quast retorted with triumph and defiance in his voice. 'That's what I volunteered for.'

The switchboard operator, who was safely out of sight, gave a broad grin. The colonel stared at Quast with his mouth ajar, a thread of spittle running from lip to lip. Ellberg looked straight through him.

Although Quast was fully kitted for combat duty within a week, his troop train for Russia was delayed. That was how he came to face with the war where he least expected it.

His pass ran till 10 P.M., and Eberhard had invited him home for supper. Eberhard's family lived in an elegant, spacious apartment overlooking the Lietzensee in Charlottenburg. Parquet floors, genuine oriental carpets, rich drapes, valuable paintings, Chinse vases, finely moulded architraves, Art Nouveau door fittings, inlaid panelling – everything exuded affluence and opulence. Quast revelled in the contrast between his present surroundings and the bleak confines of the barrack room. The meal was good, though modest compared to the silver and china that accompanied it. Like Quast's, Eberhard's father was away doing war work. His mother, very much a *grande dame*, put Quast through a detailed inquisition, but not about his own doings. All that interested her was the uncivilized environment and uncouth company inflicted on her son by army life. She soon left the boys alone together.

They were joined after supper by a friend of Eberhard's whom Quast had briefly met at interschool sports events, and by Eberhard's sister, a tomboyish teenager with short curly hair and long legs. Her studiously casual manner conveyed that no three young soldiers were going to impress *her* with their ultraprofessional talk of weapons and equipment. Margot's self-assurance appealed to Quast. He was ever so slightly bewitched by her fine brown hair and dainty hands, not to mention the fullness that tautened her blouse in such a mysteriously alluring way.

Air-raid sirens broke into their small talk and carefree

laughter. Perversely, their spirits rose even higher at this martial invasion of privacy. They switched off the phonograph, with its stack of American jazz records, and trooped – still laughing – into the cellar. Their elders, who were huddled there in overcoats and fur-lined jackets, eyed them sourly. Anti-aircraft guns began to bark a few minutes later. Then the ground shuddered under the impact of bombs. Another twenty minutes, and an agitated voice came echoing around the subterranean labyrinth: 'Incendiaries on the roof!' The three boys and Margot raced up the stairs two at a time, pursued by cries of alarm from the older folk. Reaching the attic, they found that the roof had been holed. A number of tiles were dislodged, and everything was immersed in a reddish glow. One of the incendiaries had neatly embedded itself in a box of sand kept ready for just such an emergency, another was lodged in a gutter, and two duds were lying on the floor of a servant's cramped little bedroom. They looked like octagonal vacuum flasks with fins.

But it wasn't the sight of the bombs that halted them in their tracks. The view through the rafters was breathtaking – a sea of smoke and flames stretching away to the horizon. Horrified, they made their way silently down to the street, bunched together but alone with their thoughts.

Shattered bricks, fragments of plaster, and shards of splintered glass crunched beneath their feet. Dishevelled figures flitted past with dirty, distraught faces and tousled hair. Furniture and personal belongings were being carried out into the forecourt of an apartment building whose roof was ablaze. A corner house had collapsed. Rescue workers coated with brick dust were swarming over the mound of rubble like ants, shouting hoarsely to each other as they pried chunks of masonry loose and hauled them clear. A sobbing woman crouched beside two motionless bodies sprawled on the sidewalk, their contorted limbs powdered red and white with brick dust and plaster. On the far side of the street, dense black smoke poured from a handsome house with lofty windows and a pillared portico. The window panes were bursting with a series of muffled reports. Margot pressed close to Quast's side, trembling. A red glare illuminated the drawing room's panelled walls, paintings, chandeliers, heavy velvet curtains. Then long tongues of orange flame darted from the window embrasures. The fire crackled loudly enough to drown their own hurried breathing. Quast put his arm round Margot and held her tight. She gave a sob and rested her head on his shoulder. A lump came into his throat.

There they stood, two frightened children with soot-stained cheeks, unable to grasp what was happening.

4

AUTHOR: *Didn't it strike you how barbarous the military system was?*

QUAST: *No. I thought any sytem was as good or bad as the way it was run. It's much the same in school, after all. With good teachers you work well and enjoy your lessons.*

A tramp of feet. Hobnailed boots were pounding the cobbles in step. At intervals between the marching columns, field kitchens were trundled across the platform of the freight depot, loaded on to flatcars with concerted shouts of 'Heave!' and chained and chocked into place. Stencilled inscriptions on the grimy boxcars read: '8 Horses or 30 Men'. The straw inside was so fresh and dusty that the heavy-laden soldiers coughed when they finally jostled their way up the ramp and into the semi-darkness. There was a smell of horse dung, rifle oil, leather, cookhouse bread, tobacco smoke, exhaust fumes, and clammy uniforms. The locomotive, a mighty mountain of grey-black metal, bathed the whole scene in a miasma of steam, smoke, and lubricating oil as it hissed along the full length of the interminable troop train to take its place at the head. 'Wheels Must Turn for Victory', proclaimed the white lettering on its tender, which was heaped with lustrous black coal, and long skeins of water cascaded down its battered sides. Station buildings, freight sheds, and locomotive depot – all displayed the architectural bombast of the Wilhelminian era: red and yellow brick, turrets, crenellations, and notice boards adorned with stern, long-winded injunctions in Gothic script.

The thirty men installed themselves as comfortably as they could in their cramped abode. Most were self-absorbed and surly, many on edge. As in any random assortment of individuals cooped up cheek by jowl, there were the considerate and the callous, the daydreamers and the numskulls with two left feet, the hucksters with bargains to offer, the wisecrackers, the timid, the garrulous, and the fixers who knew at once where tea, bread, and cigarettes could be had. Thirty men in transit for war . . .

Five nights later their train pulled into Gatchina. They were shivering with cold and their joints ached, because the confines of the boxcar had given them little scope for movement. Some were feeling queasy after their supper of cookhouse bread and fat salt pork. Or was it excitement? Or fear? Ponderously, the column got under way. Rifles clattered against gas-mask containers, felt-covered canteens gurgled, brand-new webbing creaked. They trudged past timber-framed houses, past convoys of artillery and supply wagons, across wide-open spaces. Flashes lit the skyline at irregular intervals. A dull rumble like the sound of a distant thunderstorm rose in volume and died away, swelled and faded: the signature tune of the Leningrad front. A barracks stood out foursquare against the night sky.

Inside, grey corridors, grey barrack rooms, rows of two-tiered grey iron bedsteads, frayed blankets, naked electric light bulbs glowing feebly. Sheeplike, they went wherever they were herded by their noncoms' raucous words of command. The high spirits that had welled up during their long hours in the train, as it does among schoolboys, had long since subsided. They were thankful to be able to discard their equipment. Half an hour later, with the jolting of the boxcar, the clank of couplings, and the rhythm of the rails in their ears, they drifted into sleep. They could still see the wrecked locomotives and freight cars beside the embankment, the off-white helmets of the railroad sentries in their little stockades, the street signs adorned with strange military emblems and code names, the signpost marked 'St Petersburg 42km – Berlin 1600km,' the thickly muffled gunners on their limbers, scorching their fingertips and knitting their brows as they strove to extract the last lungful of smoke from minuscule cigarette butts, the strain in the eyes of a lanky lieutenant, his crumpled field service cap and captured Russian submachine gun with its clumsy butt and drum magazine.

Next morning it was raining. Gusts of wind slammed the doors and tore the youngsters' curses from their lips. They were standing, once more encumbered and constricted by their equipment, on a spacious parade ground flanked by mounds of debris. Everything was grey, blackish brown, or spotty white. They caught a glimpse of shattered masonry and charred timbers, but they weren't given long to survey their surroundings. A group of men had assembled in front of them: corporals, sergeants, and a lone lieutenant. A column of soldiers in dappled camouflage suits and field service caps trudged past. One of them had a cookhouse loaf in the hood of his jacket. Helmets protruded from their hips like monstrous metallic boils, because they were wearing them on their belts with the strap looped over the ammunition pouch.

Of the men who stood facing them with such casual indifference, some wore service dress, others overcoats, and others olive drab trousers surmounted by winter battle-dress smocks with either the white or the dappled-green-and-brown side outermost. A few carried Volkhov sticks the length of an alpenstock but two or three fingers thick – black wooden staffs that were prized in proportion to the amount of intricate white carving they displayed. Beside another stood a carrier bag with the neck of a brandy bottle peeping out. All the noncoms looked pale and exhausted. The hair beneath their caps

49

was shaggy and unkempt, and all wore rubber boots smeared with greyish-white mud. Quast eagerly studied their decorations, wound badges, Iron Crosses, assault badges, Crimea badges, Romanian and Bulgarian medal ribbons. The medals themselves were tarnished and the ribbons greasy.

The veterans picked their replacements out of the ranks like traders in a slave market. 'Ten men for the 215th!' 'Sixteen for the 170th!' 'Eight for the 132nd!' 'Twelve for the 227th!' 'Ten men . . . eight men . . . twenty men . . .'

The divisional numbers meant nothing to Quast. 'Radio training?' a sergeant asked him crisply. 'Speed? Switchboard? Cable-laying?' Quast found himself assigned to a party of eight. Before long, they were sitting in a freight car surrounded by ammunition boxes. The men of the division they were joining ignored them and stared at the rain-swept desolation outside.

Quast had made himself comfortable on two mortar-bomb boxes. An icy draught blew in through the door of the freight car. They passed trans-shipment points piled high with supplies. Snow fences shielded the sidings, and one-horse carts came churning along approach roads knee-deep in brown mud. Interminable swaths of leafless birch trees swam past, bending before the wind. Quast felt curious, and a little excited. He didn't know what would happen next, but he was amenable to any order that came his way.

Had he ever had moments of doubt? Yes, but he could count them on the fingers of one hand. The first was during leadership training, when his classmate Albert Hirsch, a blond giant with a vicious left hook, had suddenly stuck a Swedish pennant on his bike and announced that he and his family were emigrating to Scandinavia. It seemed that the Jungvolk authorities were more interested in his family tree than his left hook: Albert was half Jewish. To Quast, this was no stigma. He

50

hadn't minded when Isidor Warschauer, who was no good at sport or anything else, failed to turn up for class one day and they were told that the Warschauers had gone to America. But a fine fellow like Albert? He bore absolutely no relation to what they'd been told about Jews at Jungvolk meetings. Quast could remember arguing fiercely with him, one twilit autumn afternoon, over whether or not German pocket battleships should still be equipped with stern torpedo tubes under modern battle conditions. And then Albert had fallen silent. He presented Quast with his Swedish pennant. Next day, his place in class was empty.

Quast, who didn't understand anti-Semitic propaganda and judged Jews purely on their physical prowess, found this puzzling. His uncle had once mentioned a Jewish friend with an Iron Cross First Class from the 1914–18 war. As far as Quast was concerned, this proved that not all propaganda should be taken literally – the Führer himself had said so in *Mein Kampf*.

Though shaken by his clash with Ellberg, Quast now dismissed it as a mishap. He had since become convinced that no one at the front would think or act as nonsensically as Ellberg and his ROC instructors.

And yet . . . Eighteen months earlier, he and his friend Fritz Hengst had been walking down Suarezstrasse in Charlottenburg. They were level with the fire station when Fritz said suddenly, 'By the way, I just got a letter from Peter Frille in Russia.'

'That's great. What does he say?'

Fritz peered around carefully and whispered, 'You mustn't tell a soul, word of honour?'

'Cross my heart.'

Fritz pulled a crumpled sheet of paper from his pocket and handed it over. Quast read that Peter looked back on their evening singsongs with nostalgia, and that the Russians were no pushover, especially their tanks, which were incredibly well designed and effective. The letter went on:

'We don't deserve to win this war. Terrible things are being done here in the name of our country. What Germans are doing to defenceless people, simply because they're Jews, is indescribable. When I think how we used to sing and dream of building a better, fairer world . . .'

Quast handed the letter back, appalled, and Fritz said, 'Peter always was a bit of an idealist. Something bad must have happened out there, but he can't have meant it the way it sounds, so don't breathe a word.'

Sure, Peter Frille was an idealist, but no more so than the rest of them. They'd admired him. He was cheerful and high-spirited, and he'd beguiled them all with his guitar-playing and belted out the old German mercenary songs of the seventeenth century with a zest that made them yearn for helmet, sword, and the clash of steel.

'Soldiers of fortune, sound the charge and raise your flag on high. With hearts aglow our ranks advance to conquer or to die . . .' Hurrying home through the quiet streets after a protracted singsong Quast had often sung such martial anthems under his breath.

It simply couldn't be true what Peter had written, but Quast never got a chance to ask him, because he was killed two weeks later.

And now Quast himself was in Russia, hunkered down in a supply train routed from Gatchina to Tosno. He and his companions were bound for an area described by German military geologists – such beings actually existed – as unsuitable for military operations in summer and winter alike. The serried birchwood crosses of a divisional cemetery crawled past. Women in babushkas and ragged smocks were digging graves. A stack of freshly carpentered crosses towered alongside. Quast averted his gaze. Very soon, he told himself, he would really know what went on here.

But he had to possess his soul in patience, even after they had detrained. While seasoned veterans leaned against sunwarmed timber walls, lethargically puffing at their cigarettes and pipes and happy to be left in peace, Quast went looking for excitement. He could hardly contain his thirst for action. He knelt beside a young birch tree, raised his rifle, centred his sights on the target, and squeezed the trigger. A shot rang out, and the tin can he had wedged between two twigs went spinning into the undergrowth. He felt pleased with himself.

It was thawing, and the soles of his boots became clogged with mush as he made his way along the rutted track that led out of the dripping, crackling wood. Rifle slung and hands in pockets, he trudged erratically back to the village, dodging the worst of the puddles. He passed the double grave with the weatherworn cross inscribed: 'Two Unknown German Airmen'. Overhead, birch trees were just becoming tinged with green. There was the engineers' trestle bridge with another dozen graves beside it. Prominent among them, the cross with the perforated helmet and the inscription: 'Here Lies the Toughest Sergeant in the 96th Division.'

Above the rumbling in the distance, Quast whistled softly to himself. It was Sunday morning, the fourth since he'd been assigned to No 2 Company.

He had yet to see an armed Russian. The civilians in whose wretched homes the men of No 2 were billeted led a shadowy, hand-to-mouth existence. The soldiers shrewdly exploited the older inhabitants' willingness to be of service, and the Russians – just as shrewdly – made themselves indispensable. The peasants' manner towards the Germans was timidly good-natured. The soldiers responded by being bluff but friendly, especially with children. They bought themselves little favours with bread, tobacco, and candy bars. If they weren't always liked, at least their gifts helped to mitigate the natural hatred of an invader. Newcomers thought they detected genuine compassion in the Russian crones who came to their aid with needle and thread – and indeed, some of the old women may well have felt maternal towards the overgrown children who strutted around with lethal weapons in ignorance of what they were doing.

Younger Russian women were housed in special huts, divided into working parties, and fed by field kitchens. These squads of female labourers repaired roads, felled timber, and dug graves in which they doubtless hoped their guards would soon be lying.

Quast had learned that he was a 'replacement'. All his eager questions notwithstanding, he was seldom included in the conversational exchanges between his comrades in Sergeant Max's signal section. The jargon they spoke was a product of shared experience, of combat itself, and they laughed at catchwords that meant nothing to him. No one felt inclined to explain them or try to bridge the light-years that separated young Quast from the 'old gang', as the newcomers called them. Some of them had actually turned thirty.

But there were other disadvantages in being a replacement. For a start, replacements had to exchange their well-maintained rifles from armouries back home for company-supplied carbines. They soon found out why. Their duties comprised equipment maintenance, radio instruction (which Quast particularly enjoyed because army psychologists had tested him just before he left for Russia and pronounced him an ideal radio operator, coupling their verdict with a demand to know what idiot had assigned him to field telephony), drilling in ankle-deep mud, carrying brimful pails of stew for the entire platoon across a flooded footbridge over the swirling Tigoda, kit inspections, helping to maintain the company's motley vehicle fleet (with awestruck glances at windshields and coachwork punctured by bullets and shell splinters), and – last but not least – arms inspections.

They paraded in all innocence, barrels carefully pulled through, stocks conscientiously rubbed with rifle oil.

'For inspection, port . . . arms! Remove your bolts, thumbnails in the breech!'

Company Sergeant Major Briegel was taking the trouble to peer down their barrels in person. And then it came: 'What's this meant to be?'

'A 98K carbine, Sergeant Major.'

'Bullshit! I want to know where that rust came from.'

'That's how it was when I got it from the armourer, Sergeant Major.'

'What! Don't try and tell me you were issued a wreck like that in *this* company. Sergeant, take this man's name. Two weeks' extra guard duty.'

The replacements were speechless. For reasons that became blindingly obvious, the same fate befell them all. It was they who had to stand guard at night, pacing the muddy village street and peering into the darkness with eyes stung to tears by rain and snow. Such was the unwritten law. By rights, everyone in the company was liable to stand guard, but if all who scored a black mark were given extra guard duty, the rest could be exempted. Replacements were doomed to score black marks. They were allotted rifles that had been salvaged from mud and water by general order, processed by repair shops in exchange for special allocations of vodka, and reissued. The mud had been washed off and the damaged components replaced, but the rust? Rust didn't matter when an enemy was fifty yards away or less, but anyone who paraded for arms inspection with a rusty barrel had his name taken. And the replacements had their names taken again and again.

A stormy night. Quast was on watch between 2 and 4 A.M. – the worst spell of all – with a fellow replacement named Oskar. From somewhere nearby came a spasmodic hammering sound. A door or window being battered against its frame by the gusts? No, it came from the abandoned bunker beside the muddy village street.

'Oskar, see if you can stop that noise. I'll stay here, but don't be long.'

Oskar disappeared. Quast stood there shivering and shuffling from foot to foot. Minutes went by, and still no sign of Oskar. Quast walked over to the bunker entrance and called. No answer. What was he up to down there? Had he run into a lurking partisan, or was he snatching a smoke – or snoozing?'

'Oskar!'

Still no answer. Quast flipped his safety catch and tiptoed down the steps, then shone the flashlight round the corner. There was Oskar with cigarette smoke dribbling from his nostrils.

'You jerk! Come out of there.'

That was when the guard commander gave tongue behind them. 'That's what I like to see: two young gentlemen skulking down here instead of guarding their comrades. No wonder I spent hours looking for you all over the village. Well, you know what's coming to you.'

They knew all right, just as they knew it was no use explaining. Though stung by the sergeant's stupid exaggerations, they were happy to get off with five weeks' extra guard duty apiece – always between 2 and 4 A.M., naturally.

One night when Quast couldn't sleep because he felt cheated and wasted eight miles behind the lines, he dipped into the guard commander's log. The carbide lamp hissed softly, and snores issued from the other bunks. Oskar was muttering in his sleep. The air reeked of stale smoke and cold cigarette butts.

'Sergeant Gustav Heberle discovered in bed with a Russian girl in Hut No 2,' he read. It was the first time Heberle's name had registered with him. They'd been taught that anyone entering either of the female labourers' huts would be severely punished, but what had Heberle done? He, the hated invader, had blithely climbed into a Russian's bed. He owed his discovery to a random check. The women hadn't raised the alarm; on the contrary, it was clear from the guard commander's report that they'd tried to hide him. Heberle's visit seemed to have met with their approval. Strange, thought Quast. In his experience, the girls in the road gangs never even gave their German masters a sidelong glance. Heberle, he concluded, must be quite a guy.

5

AUTHOR: *Didn't you feel scared when you got to the front?*

QUAST: *Scared? Sure, we all were. The way I saw it, there was no virtue in being brave if you didn't get the shakes first.*

AUTHOR: *But the sight of death . . .*

QUAST: *I simply didn't have the imagination to picture myself lying there. If we were more imaginative, the world might be a safer place. Don't you agree?*

Mid-April. First Lieutenant Strehling, their shrewd, sharp-tongued, shirt-sleeved company commander, was on leave. Second Lieutenant Schuster, a young man who looked like a cross between an accountant and a country parson, was deputizing for him. The new additions lined up in front of the company. Schuster gave them each a vigorous handshake. Then he addressed them in stirring tones. Doing their duty by the Fatherland, proving their mettle, standing their ground . . . Quast sighed. He was feeling grouchy – sick of high-flown phrases. They'd been promoted signallers first class, but who cared? Staring up at the spring sky, Quast longed for some stroke of fate to deliver him from the clutches of official-dom. Fine words were no consolation.

They fell out and rejoined the rest of the company. The ceremonial part of the parade was over. Sergeant Major Briegel started to read out instructions, orders, and transfers. High above, a reconnaissance plane went about its leisurely business. The sun, which was shining on the soldier's backs, penetrated their coarse woollen shirts.

'Division has decided to form another intercept detachment,' Briegel was saying. 'You know what a valuable job these teams have done in the past, so . . . Volunteers, step forward.' He paused and looked up. 'What, no one?'

Quast glanced at the others. No matter how slowly and persuasively Briegel scanned the ranks, their insolent air of unruffled boredom persisted. 'Volunteer?' they seemed to be saying. 'Not likely!'

'Very well,' said Briegel. 'You can have till thirteen hundred hours.'

'What's an intercept detachment?' Quast whispered to the man beside him.

His neighbour gave him the thumbs down. 'Suicide squad' was his terse response.

'Any of you been in one?'

'We wouldn't be here now if we had. They never come back.'

Another of the old gang's tall stories, thought Quast, who knew at last how he was going to inject some colour into his drab existence. Ten minutes later, he marched into the gloom of the peasant cottage where Sergeant Major Briegel was temporarily waging his desk war.

'Well, Quast, come to collect your chevrons straight from the orderly room?'

'No, Sergeant Major.' Quast drew a deep breath. 'Signaller Quast begs permission to join the intercept detachment.'

The orderly-room clerk put his pencil down and stared.

'Hm,' Briegel said slowly. 'A volunteer, eh?' Something glimmered in his cold yellow eyes. For a moment, Quast suspected him of being human after all. 'Very well, be outside here in full combat order at sixteen hundred. You can pick up your marching orders then. All clear, Signaller Quast?'

'As daylight, Sergeant Major.'

Relieved and exhilarated, Quast faced about. Something was happening at last. He was accosted outside the door by someone he knew only by sight.

'Hello, Quast. My name's Hassel. I've just joined Heberle's outfit too.'

'You don't mean *he's* in charge? That's terrific!'

Quast felt as if he'd hit the jackpot. He doubled back to his billet and flung the door open. Sergeant Max and the rest of the signal section were ensconced at the table, spooning up their midday meal. Some of them were in undershirts and braces, and one was wearing a hideous civilian sweater. Quast's brimming mess kit was perched on the end of the table.

'Your grub's gone cold,' said Max. 'Where've you been?'

The others didn't look up.

'I'm moving out, Sergeant. I've joined the intercept detachment.'

They all paused in mid mouthful, lowered their folding spoons, and stared at him. Max got up.

'You mean you've already been to the orderly room?'

'Yes, Sergeant.'

'Hell, then there's no use discussing it. Let's get down to cases. Are you all right for underwear? What about socks? Got a decent sweater? Those boots of yours are much too big. You'll have to run in them, don't forget.'

The others rose and rummaged in their kit. From one minute to the next, Quast became the possessor of new undershirts and socks without darns. They addressed him by his first name, eyed him curiously, swapped his torn old shelter half for a new one, and presented him with a pair of foot wraps, 'for the swamps'. And when at last he set ponderously forth, laden like a pack mule, they gathered in the narrow doorway and slapped him on the back.

'Don't be too goddamned keen, sonny . . . Look out for number one . . . Keep your head down . . .'

Quast plodded on his way, musing. They were nice guys in their own peculiar fashion.

By ten to four, the intercept detachment was waiting on the sandy track outside the orderly room, five men in all. Herberle himself – thickset, medium height, ruddy cheeks, broad smile, pale grey eyes, big hands, deliberate and purposeful movements, nothing staccato about him, more an athlete's loose-limbed poise – looked his men over like a farmer buying a team of oxen. He'd made inquiries about them, of course. Now he compared reports with reality. Little Quast – a scrawny child peering inquisitively through steel-rimmed glasses, touchingly ready and eager to accept any challenge, touchingly ignorant of what lay ahead – didn't look much like a soldier. With a sigh, Heberle turned to the others. Next, Hapf, lean and angular, awkward and edgy, with a pointed chin and small mouth. Then Hassel, a high school graduate from Heidelberg, tall and muscular, with rosy cheeks, big horn-rimmed glasses, a snub nose, and slightly protruding eyes. Finally, Sand, a chain-smoking Rhinelander, plump and easygoing, always grinning and full of repartee.

'The interpreters'll be joining us at the radio briefing centre,' Heberle said, glancing at his black-faced wristwatch. They stood there rather casually at the eyes left while Heberle, also rather casually, gave notice of his team's departure to Sergeant Major Briegel. There seemed little love lost between the two noncoms, and Quast was not the only one to give the sergeant major a triumphant grin as they dumped their equipment in a two-wheeled cart and Heberle at last ordered, 'Right face, route step, march!' Briegel turned and disappeared into his log cabin.

Black wisps of cloud hung low in the sky, which was turning greenish pink. Trees and undergrowth exhaled a chill, damp breath as the shadows lengthened. Audible above the never-ending thunder on the horizon, twigs and dry leaves rustled in a gentle breeze. The cart creaked, the men plodded along in silence, the village sank behind the treetops.

* * *

The briefing centre lay buried in the woods some distance from the fortified village. It was cramped and dark inside. The men were seated on makeshift benches and ammunition boxes. Leaning against a narrow plank table stood Sergeant Hansen, the expert who was to enlighten them on their future role. Hansen accompanied his words with graceful gestures. He was a slight, sensitive-looking man whose long hair brushed the yellow scarf that overflowed his uniform collar. He might have been lecturing on the fine arts as he spoke, not of danger and violence, but of guile, dexterity, patience, and intuition. Despite his unassuming manner, this precision engineer in uniform made a deep impression on them all – even Sergeant Lieven, a cool, cynical Balt, and Hans, an ex-Red Army man from the Volga German Autonomous Soviet Socialist Republic, both of whom had been assigned to the detachment as interpreters.

At last they heard what the score was. To their dismay, they were warned to cherish no illusions about their secret mission. The equipment delivered by Germany to Russia under the non-aggression pact of 1939 had included, among many other things, a hundred-odd intercept receivers, so there was a chance that they themselves would be monitored and attacked. They were also told of the ambushes and booby traps to which other detachments had fallen prey. Having brought them down to earth, Hansen put them in the picture.

'We monitor enemy phone conversations from forward positions, using this gadget here, called the LE40. It's just an ultrasensitive receiver.' He indicated the grey box beside him, which resembled a clumsy, thirties radio set. 'From the LE40, heavy cable is laid above ground in loops as near as possible to the Russians' main line of defence and led back to the receiver. The best place is where there's a bulge, either in their line or ours. That means our loop will be running parallel to the Ivans' field telephone lines at the maximum number of points. You follow?'

They nodded. 'What then?' Quast asked eagerly.

'First things first,' said Hansen. 'Our loop picks up all the signals leaking into the ground. It's as damp as a washhouse out here in the marshes, and that suits the current fine. It doesn't give a damn about them or us – it roams around wherever the going's good. Meantime, our loop picks up signals passing through the ground and the cables within its range. All that happens inside the cable is what happens when you speak into a telephone in the ordinary way, and that you know about. The point is, as I say, that part of the current penetrates the layers of insulation and radiates in all directions. Insulation frays in the course of time, or it gets torn by shell splinters, or it simply becomes old and brittle. Anyway, the current leaks into the ground, and these leakage currents are what we amplify with our LE40' – Hansen tapped the grey box – 'and listen in to.' He paused to extract a cigarette from a crumpled pack. Then he said, 'There's a snag, of course. The loop has to run close enough to the Ivans to pick up as much as possible as clearly as possible, but far away enough for us not to trip over them when we go looking for faults. Monitoring isn't a soft job for you interpreters, either. You pick up a whole raft of conversations, naturally – loud, faint, clear, distorted, Russian, German. You have to learn to sort them out.'

To convince themselves, they carried the device out into the marshes and set it up not far from the transmission poles and cables bordering the local supply route. Then they put on their headsets and blinked. Clear as a bell, the voices that assailed their ears might have been issuing from a normal field telephone. Conversations between unit commanders, quarter-masters, and air liaison officers, orders, smutty stories, inquiries, complaints, curses, laughter – they heard them all at first hand. Hansen had not been exaggerating.

What did strike them as overdone was the way Heberle tested them ad nauseam on their ability to move silently and make use of cover. They would hardly be venturing into no-man's-land by day, and all cats were grey in the dark – or as grey as the 'white nights' peculiar to a northern land closer to the Arctic Circle than it was to Berlin. Heberle sent them across open ground in single file, periodically yelling, 'Flare!' This was the signal for them to freeze, instantly, in whatever pose he happened to catch them. They stood like tailors' dummies, feeling sheepish, and if any of them winced when stung by the myriad insects swirling around them, Heberle would shout himself hoarse and accuse them of risking their comrades' lives.

Why? On account of the Russian flares sent up over no-man's-land – flares whose chalky light was reputed to show up the slightest movement. They didn't accept this at face value, dismissing it as one more example of the same old self-dramatizing hysteria nurtured by instructors back home and veterans back at base.

Vapour enveloped the woods like grey cotton. A light rain had been falling for hours, ever since their dawn departure. The cart was a help at first, but later, when they abandoned the supply route for a forest track surfaced with logs, they had to unload their packs, blankets, receiver, batteries, cable drums, rifles, gas masks, shelter halves, haversacks, and canteens. Everthing was clammy and slippery, every leather strap bloated with moisture. The driver gave them a farewell grunt, reined his horse round, and vanished into the mist. They stood there in the mud, eyeing each other sullenly, before setting off. A gun tractor picked them up and took them part of the way. Then they were back on the greasy, uneven corduroy road with water welling up between the logs underfoot. Curses flew whenever someone slipped and collided with his neighbours, and the rain on their faces became mingled with sweat. Quast, whose glasses were forever misting over, could hardly see.

It was their first operational mission, but none of them

spared a thought for that. They barely noticed that more and more trees had been lopped or scarred by shell bursts and splinters, just as it barely occurred to them that a few yards of fencing, stone hearth, or wagon wheel in the undergrowth beside the track might mark the site of a village where people had once lived in peace.

Their periodic halts for a mouthful of bread and a swig of lukewarm coffee were brief. Their limbs soon stiffened in the cold and damp, so they pressed on. Then they saw the first circular pools beside the track: shell holes. Discarded remnants of splintered logs, recently replaced with fesh-hewn timber, showed how accurate the Russian fire had been. Posts bearing tactical signs began to appear. The thunder on the horizon had long since become a swelling, fading staccato of separate reports and explosions. Above the hiss of the rain, they heard what sounded like a flock of wild geese come whirring through the sky from their rear. 'Twenty-ones,' Heberle said laconically,' – 'ours.' And then, long after they'd ceased to expect it, they heard the hollow crump of shells bursting in the forest far ahead.

A jeep raced past, spattering them with mud. They could hardly summon up the energy to curse. Heberle studied some signposts and gestured to the right, up a gently ascending track through the woods. They came to some low mounds of earth with shattered trees overhead. In front of them stood a dispatch rider with a cigarette dangling from the corner of his mouth and rain dripping off his helmet, and beside him a sentry in a shelter half. Shivering and exhausted, they dumped their gear on the ground and waited. Out of the wet and into the dry was their overriding thought. Heberle, who had vanished into a dugout, surfaced with a staff sergeant in tow: stained uniform, no belt, collar turned up, chin strap raised. He gave them a brief, expressionless glance. 'That one was meant for you,' Quast heard him say. He pointed to a mound of earth in a nearby clearing. Jutting from it in all directions were heavy balks of rent and splintered timber. 'Direct hit this morning. Four men killed.'

That was why the earth looked so churned up and the surrounding trees so strangely bedraggled. A little farther on was another mound, roofed with two layers of thick logs whose ends could just be seen through a topping of soil. They stumbled down the narrow steps. The interior was so cramped that they got in each other's way while struggling out of their sodden equipment. A tiny stove, improvised out of an old tin can and some strips of metal, gave off a hint of warmth. A corporal, jacket unbuttoned, was sitting at the end of the plank that served as a table. Levering open a can of sardines with his bayonet, he dipped some bread in the oil and chewed, watching them quizzically as they blundered around in their efforts to undo buttons, hooks, and buckles with clammy fingers. Heberle said, 'I'm going up front to see how the land lies. Our operational dugout won't be vacant till tomorrow morning. The guide's expecting us.' At that moment, above the whisper of the rain, which was easing off, they heard a peculiar noise. It sounded like a dozen corks being pulled in quick succession.

The corporal, whose sleeve – they were awed to note – was adorned with a tank-destruction badge, stopped chewing.

'Better wait a while.'

'Why?' said Heberle.

'Evening serenade,' said the corporal, and stuffed a sardine into his mouth.

Almost simultaneously, there was an earsplitting crash and the dugout lurched. They fell to their knees. Outside, splinters, clods of earth, and branches thudded into the mire. The corporal selected another sardine. Again the distant corks popped, and again the earth shuddered. The dugout door flapped on its hinges. Footsteps squelched past overhead and a voice said loudly, 'Screw the Ivans!' Rifle fire rattled in the distance like hail on a tin roof.

Then silence descended. The rain had stopped. The corporal lit a cigarette and nodded to Heberle, who turned and said, 'Won't be long.' The others sat there on their bunks, too scared and exhausted to speak.

The corporal sat back and shut his eyes, alternately picking his teeth and smoking. Some minutes later he groped inside his grimy undershirt and extracted something. He raised one eyelid and inspected it. There was a faint crack. He shut his eye again, belched, and instantly fell asleep. Glinting on his jacket were the infantry assault badge, the Iron Cross First Class, and the wound badge in silver.

Despite himself, Quast started scratching as soon as he realized that he had just witnessed the extermination of a louse by a maestro. He was puzzled. They looked quite different, the heroes they'd admired in the newsreels back home.

6

AUTHOR: *Didn't you feel utterly insignificant, out there in the forests and marshes?*

QUAST: *On the contrary, I genuinely thought I counted for something. But then, don't we all overrate ourselves? It's part of being young.*

'These long, oval things are sandy ridges, not loaves of bread.' Heberle traced their outlines on the map with a blade of grass. 'There are pine trees and bushes on them and swamp grass all around – that's the yellowy-green stuff. We were dug in along there till last winter. Then the Ivans broke through – here and here and here. They overran our forward positions, so we had to fall back on our second line of defence. The Ivans installed themselves in our first line – walled up the dugout entrances or converted them into firing positions and dug new entrances into them from their own side of the fence – and we upgraded our second-string dugouts into a forward line. This bulge here – that's where the Ivans drove a wedge into our territory, up as far as the forest and across that open ground. That's why our line kinks so sharply. And that kink' – Heberle tapped the map with his blade of grass – 'is where our dugout is. All the Ivans' telephone lines run past it, forward to their command posts and artillery observers and back to their battalion HQs and gun emplacements. That's a point in our favour – if we lay some loops there, we can't fail to pick something up – but it isn't an unmixed blessing. Our little salient is a thorn in the Ivans' side, so they try to nip it off now and then.

That's why we keep a machine-gun nest right next door to the dugout. Well, that's all you need to know for now.' Heberle looked from face to face. 'Any questions?'

Hapf put his hand up. 'How far away are they?'

'The opposition? In front of the dugout, eighty or ninety yards, but it's all thick with craters and wire. An eel couldn't wriggle through.'

'And the flanks?' asked Quast.

'Open to infiltration, so they say.' Heberle pointed to the map again. 'Here about a hundred yards, here two hundred. Here fifty maximum, but the ground's a quagmire.'

Hassel said, 'What about the mines?'

'Our own minefield maps have been lost or destroyed. As for the Ivans' hardware . . .' Heberle shrugged. 'We'll have to watch our step, that's all.' He lit a cigarette with his windproof lighter, a sign that the briefing was over, and deliberately refolded the map. The others preserved a thoughtful silence.

Heberle had gone forward a second time during the night. Now, at dawn, his detachment set off, carrying only the bare essentials of their equipment. They were guided by a beanpole of a sergeant with a stick grenade in one boot and his helmet swinging from its strap like a shopping basket. It soon became clear how meagre and incomplete Heberle's briefing had been. No mention of unpredictable harassing fire by Russian mortars, of the hiss just prior to impact, of vicious explosions that sent splinters humming low over the ground, or shock waves that took your breath away. No mention of marshy black pools spanned by narrow, precarious footbridges. No mention, either, of the fact that parts of the route between dugouts and guard posts were unprotected from the rifle and machine-gun fire that pattered into the branches overhead.

The trees had been shorn off some ten or twelve feet from the ground. Strung between them were lengths of wire supporting pine saplings and bushes the height of a man, either interwoven or propped against them – visual protection but nothing more. Every twenty to fifty yards, a dugout or firing position lay half submerged in the morass like the back of a turtle. Heberle and his men had to negotiate a path running parallel to this screen of foliage. Quast now knew why the sergeant's nocturnal excursion had left him breathless and caked with mud. From time to time, when a flare went up or drifted down by parachute, their guide signalled to them to freeze. Holes had been blown in the screen, so any movement behind it would have been visible enough at such close range to attract a hail of enemy fire.

The dugout at last: timber-roofed, with a blast wall of rough-hewn logs shielding the steps and the entrance at their foot. A low voice called, 'Halt, who goes there?' and the guide answered, 'Königsberg'. Russian fire could come from almost any direction. This explained why the sentry mounted guard in the sunken entrance, not beside it, and why the protective wall had been erected.

The interior was painfully cramped and reeked of mildew. Narrow bunks, filthy woollen blankets, a makeshift oil-drum stove encrusted with burned bread crumbs, duckboards awash with stinking swamp water. Weapons hung from nails driven into the walls and uprights, which glistened with moisture. Ammunition boxes, mess kits, carbide lamps, and Hindenburg candles – night lights in cardboard cups – lay everywhere. Amorphous bundles of snoring humanity occupied the two-tiered bunks, some of which were recessed while others protruded into the rectangular chamber. Pinned to the wall was a panoramic map on which Quast identified the words 'Burma Road', and beside it were a pair of battery commander's binoculars. From one of the supports, just below the dripping roof timbers, hung a crumpled second lieutenant's cap with red artillery piping – evidence that the dugout had some sitting tenants in the shape of an artillery observer and his radio operator.

Hurriedly, they threw off their packs and stowed their equipment. Then came a sudden lull. For one brief moment, they stopped short and stared at each other, all struck by the same thought: They were there at last – up front and all set to go.

Every morning at 0600, one of them would make his way back to Battalion Headquarters with Heberle's report on the night's activities. A dispatch rider would then take the original and one copy to the divisional intelligence officer and on to corps headquarters. Every morning they would take their buckets and bail out the water that had risen above the duckboards overnight. Every day between 1200 and 1500, one of them would fetch rations and mail and deliver an interim report detailing what operations the detachment proposed to undertake during the night. The afternoons would be devoted to maintaining weapons and equipment, the nights to repairing cables severed by enemy fire. Such was the gist of Heberle's preliminary report to Battalion Headquarters next day – matter-of-fact phrases signifying that an intercept detachment was in position and doing its job.

Quast who had crept to an observation slit, surveyed the dugout's approaches in the morning light. Over there, where the tangle of branches thickened and pale green foliage yielded by degrees to brown and black, were the Russians. Beyond lay a dark backdrop of forest overhung by a misty sky the colour of buttermilk. The yellow spine of a sandy ridge turned grey where it merged with the marshes. Clumps of reeds rustled in a May breeze laden with the mingled scents of decay, resin, spent explosive, and rotting vegetation.

Quast listened to the whiplash of rifle fire, the rattle of automatic weapons, the vicious crump of mortar bombs, the undulating echoes that dwindled to a rumbling basso profundo as they rolled away into the forest, the rending crash of high-explosive shells. He heard rats scrabbling in the undergrowth, wind whispering in the grass, splinters and slivers of wood tearing through such twigs as remained on the trees. He heard fading cries, scraps of conversation, rubber boots splashing through stagnant water, the clatter of weapons and ammunition boxes, the drone and rumble of supply columns on both sides of the line. Eruptions of noise were punctuated by sudden, ominous silences, and into them – though Quast could hardly believe his ears – crept sounds of incongruous sweetness: the 'chak-chak-chak' of the thrush, the 'chink-chink-chink' and anxious 'chook' of the blackbird, and the thin 'sissi-sissi-sissi' of the coal tit. He hoped the poor little creatures were only passing through. Hard as it was to tear himself away, he crawled back into the dugout.

Two hours later, having just delivered a routine report from Heberle, Quast was perched on a tree stump near Battalion Headquarters. He was delousing himself as swiftly as possible to prevent the mosquitoes from settling on his bare hide. He smirked at Sergeant Major Briegel's departing figure, reliving every moment of their latest encounter.

Briegel had come to check on the welfare of No 2 Company's prodigal sons. His manner was uncharacteristically mild. He shot nervous glances in all directions, looked on with furrowed brow as a party of walking wounded limped past, and turned pale when a shell landed in the trees only fifty yards away – a blowout whose lethal contents discharged themselves with a long, hollow, harmless roar.

'Need anything, Signaller Quast?'

'Like what, Sergeant Major?'

'Well, stuff from the canteen?'

'Oh, I get you. Sure, I'd like some decent cigars. Not the kind the CO offers me when we have our morning powwow – they're too strong for me. I prefer mine light and mild but full of flavour – only the best, you understand.'

'Perfectly, Quast.'

'I need some razor blades, too. The Ivans don't fancy Germans with stubble trouble.'

'But of course, my dear Quast, right away.'

Briegel had actually called him his 'dear' Quast. And then, from above their heads, came the shuffling, slithering sound of a thousand sleds being hauled across gravel. Briegel flinched and hit the dirt; Quast didn't budge.

'Get up, Sergeant Major, they're ours.'

Briegel had bidden him a frosty farewell while the ground shook and mushrooms of smoke billowed behind the Russian lines. Quast laughed aloud at the recollection and pulled on his faded, sweat-stained shirt.

Midday. Sunlight probed the greenery and sprinkled white flecks on the path that led through the wilderness. The path itself consisted of logs the thickness of a man's arm nailed crosswise to balks of rough-hewn timber. It floated on the morass like a ladder on ice, spreading its load over as large an expanse as possible. The ladder didn't sink, even though the water beneath Quast gurgled and sloshed at every step he took. His helmet was smeared with mud and its paintwork scoured around the rim. The strap was hard and dark with sweat. His camouflage jacket, of coarse, dappled-green material, hung loose, emphasizing his slender shoulders. Crusts of dried mud adhered to his black rubber boots and the knees of his olive drab trousers. His silhouette merged with the tracery of foliage around him.

He would have to take care when he came to the racetrack, he told himself. Even here on the corduroy path his movements were nimble, noiseless, and wary. All the denizens of this jungle, Russian and German alike, developed the same antennae. Whatever they were doing – even sleeping – the need to forestall a fatal surprise kept their senses alert. Quast had now reached a sector where the trees had not only lost their tops but were gashed and riven by shellfire. The air should have smelled

73

of sap and resin, but the winter fighting had left hundreds of dead to decompose beneath the tangled branches like the twigs and leaves and pine needles that shared their marshy resting place. The area was thick with mines, so their bodies could not be buried. Quast had already ceased to notice the sweetish smell of rotting flesh. It was as much a part of the scene as the shrill whine of numberless mosquitoes, the sound of shots and shell bursts. Logs creaked and water spurted up whenever his boots slipped, and each time, he gritted his teeth and readjusted the knapsack he had packed so carefully beside the supply truck half an hour before. First the loaves of bread and cans of margarine, then the cured sausage and canteens of coffee, then the mail and the report forms. Tucked into the middle, a roll of insulating tape. His arms were stiffly extended because he was carrying three mess kits in each hand. They were filled to the brim but lidless, this being the only way he could manage three in one fist. The thin wire handles bit into his flesh. Perspiration seared his brow, but he couldn't wipe it away. Slowly, the salty drops crawled into the sweat rag around his neck.

For a moment, he paused. The corduroy path spanned a shallow, circular depression and came to an end. The ground on the far side was firmer, like an elastic skin stretched over the marshy subsoil. He'd reached the racetrack, a clearing easily wide enough to accommodate ten men abreast. Its gentle incline culminated in a sandy hillock that stood out yellow against the surrounding vegetation. Until last winter, men had probably breathed a sigh of relief when they reached this clearing, but now the hill was in Russian hands. Snipers couldn't lurk there – they'd have had to climb trees to gain a field of fire, and the five decapitated pines still standing there were as bare as telegraph poles – but an observer in the undergrowth could clearly see if someone was moving down below. What happened then depended on circumstances – on the observer's mood and the Russians' stock of ammunition.

Quast drew a deep breath, his heart pounding. Then he set off, darting at random from one side of the clearing to the other, zigzagging as he headed for the dead ground at the foot of the yellow hill. He was over halfway there when something barked beyond it – once, twice, six times in succession. There was a sound like the wingbeats of a giant bird. Quick as a flash, he threw himself headlong, landing on his elbows to avoid jolting and spilling the mess kits. The knapsack slid forward and knocked his helmet over his eyes. Splinters cleft the air with a razor-sharp hiss. The crisp detonation of the last mortar bomb merged with the echoes of its predecessors and went rolling through the forest like thunder. Quast was temporarily deafened. A tang of explosive mingled with the scent of damp soil and resinous wood. He lay there, motionless as a beetle playing dead. Then he scrambled up, swayed, recovered his balance, and ran on as fast as he could. A few more steps, and he was in dead ground. Even before the echoes died away, peace had returned to the sunlit clearing. Wisps of smoke rose from six shallow craters freshly scooped from the moist and glistening earth.

Quast was now panting along behind a dense latticework of foliage. A noodle and a few strands of meat were drying on the back of his right hand, and hot coffee was trickling down his back from a punctured canteen in the knapsack. The uniform clung to his perspiring body. He ran unsteadily on, tripping over snarled white roots, vaulting muddy pools, brushing past branches flayed bare of bark. Two heavy mortar bombs shuffled overhead. Harassing fire only, but their thunderous impact shook the ground and reverberated through the shell-torn trees.

He stumbled down the dugout steps. His chest heaved and his heart pounded, but his sweat-streaked face was radiant and his eyes were shining as they had shone on sports day eighteen months before, when he had come home first in the three thousand metres.

7

AUTHOR: *Are you proud of having belonged to a suicide squad?*
QUAST: *I'm thankful to have survived.*

Eighteen months before, Quast would have poured scorn on anyone who predicted that a pair of four-hundred-yard cables would one day constitute his world – that he would guard them like crown jewels and come to know every inch of them, every repair in them, like the back of his hand. But that was what happened.

It began when they laid a practice loop inside their own lines. Even then they were impressed by the vulnerability of such a simple length of cable and exasperated by the frequency with which bullets and shell splinters contrived to fracture something less than one tenth of an inch in diameter.

Now, on this milk-mild evening in early summer, they were about to repeat the process in earnest. First came a change of clothing. Trousers, camouflage jackets, and rubber boots were all they wore – plus, in Quast's case, his black Jungvolk scarf. They would get soaked to the skin. They would have to crawl, maybe jump, maybe stand up to their chests in water, so undershirts would only weigh them down. A gentle breeze was blowing, and the stench of death hung heavy over the forest. The sun's slanting rays struck the row of empty vodka bottles in the narrow slit below the roof timbers, which stood proxy for a window, flooding the dugout with greenish twilight. The inmates of the dank cavern called it the rats' nest and disliked it for all kinds of reasons, not least the smell of mould, the lack of space, the moisture that permeated every scrap of material, and the bloodstains on the bunks. These dated from last winter, when the dugout had been used as a first-aid post. The strips of adhesive tape that had served as directional aids still clung, faded now, to neighbouring tree stumps, and beside the mound lay an *akya*, one of the boat-shaped plywood sleds used for transporting wounded in winter. Whorls of stained bandage snaked from the soft earth around the dugout.

They removed their insignia in case the worst happened and the enemy's suspicions were aroused – after all, what would Signal Corps personnel be doing in no-man's-land? The first-aid pack in the left-hand trouser pocket was accompanied by five rounds of rifle ammunition in a cartridge clip. Another five rounds in the right-hand pocket, a stick grenade in one boot, combination pliers in the left-hand pocket of the camouflage jacket, cable cutter and insulating tape in the right. Nothing must be forgotten and everything stowed in such a way as not to clink or rattle.

Heberle cocked his head and listened. Then he said, 'Too much wind. No helmets.' Wind whistled in helmets and made it hard to hear telltale sounds. They also discarded their belts, which obstruct a man's breathing and hamper him when crawling. 'Hand in your things,' said Heberle, ' – paybooks, letters, photos.' Quast had seen a memo from Army Group at Battalion Headquarters. It read: 'I would again draw your attention to the fact that personnel engaged in reconnaissance patrols and similar operations must discard anything likely to reveal what unit they belong to. This includes private correspondence and documents from which enemy Intelligence might draw useful conclusions. It must be impressed on all ranks that anyone who furnishes the Russians with an opportunity to identify the Army Post Office numbers of the units facing them will be betraying his comrades.'

They surrendered their buff folders with the German eagle on the front. One of them – Sand's – was torn and distended by a sheaf of funny postcards. Quast guffawed at the sight of it, but the others didn't even smile. Hapf's was reinforced along the spine and edges with adhesive tape. With it came a group photo, each figure bearing a microscopic number corresponding to a name on the back. Only Hapf could have been so painfully precise and finicky. Now the next paybook, thick with additional pages and covered with rubber stamps. Snapshots, too: girls in evening gowns, girls in swimsuits, girls with mops of curls, girls with buns. Heberle's . . . Sand whistled through his teeth. Heberle said, 'Can it!' Then: 'Wake up, Quast.' Quast gave a start and pulled out his virginal-looking paybook, together with a pink envelope addressed in an unformed hand and a snapshot of a fair-haired girl in braids. Sand grinned and Heberle cleared his throat. Only Hassel failed to be amused by these insights into his companions' private lives. He gave them all an envious glance – envious because he was being left behind till next time out – and sullenly gathered up their belongings.

Quast's heart was in his mouth as he climbed over the parapet of the firing position. Strange: however little protection the German line afforded, he'd always had a sense of being among his own. Now he was venturing into no-man's-land. He knew that the sentries had been warned not to shoot. Two machine guns were to dispel suspicion by pumping intermittent bursts into the air without tracer, to disguise their line of fire. Ememy bullets were pattering aimlessly into the undergrowth. 'Everyone out?' whispered Heberle. 'Let's go.' The sentry winked and raised his hand. Then the bulge of his helmet disappeared behind the parapet.

The mist that always swathed the forest like a cloth after sunset had lifted far enough for the men to be visible as dark but crisply silhouetted figures from the waist down.

The rest of them dissolved into vaporous obscurity. Reeds and coarse grass sprouted from between the jumbled tree trunks and branches underfoot. The ground itself was a spongy, floating crust. Quast proceeded at a crouch, his eyes repeatedly straying from Heberle, who was slinking along ahead of him, to the next patch of ground where his foot would fall. Gingerly shifting his weight from boot to boot, he steadily unreeled cable from the drum on the wooden spindle in his hands and let it run back between his legs to Hapf, who pressed it loosely into place. Behind Hapf came Sand, covering their flanks and rear. Whenever Heberle pointed right or left or doubled back, Quast paused to relay the signal to Hapf and Sand. Mines! Washed out of the ground by rain, they could be metallic grey disks, or housed in rotting wooden boxes, or red with rust and lurking under whippy branches, or – another type like a bean can with a detonator protruding from the lid – harnessed to a pair of trip wires that increased a prospective victim's chances of self-destruction.

They had reached the Russian wire. Quast watched Heberle sidle across a suspended tree trunk. With a sudden crack, the wood gave way, pitching Heberle into the quagmire beneath. They froze. The nearest Russian sentry was only thirty or forty yards away – he must have heard the splash. Heberle was already up to his waist in slime. Quast darted forward, relieved him of his submachine gun, put it down within reach, and gave him an anxious nod. Heberle clamped a hand over his mouth: not a word! Quast's feet sank in, ankle-deep, as he braced himself and heaved. With a sucking sound, the sergeant struggled clear. They all lay still, hugging the ground. Any moment now, the machine gun whose muzzle flashes were flickering nervously on their left – God, thought Quast, that was close! – would traverse in their direction. But no, it continued to chatter malevolently at the German line.

It was when they got up and sneaked round the danger

79

spot that they saw, looming beside them, the mortar that became one of their landmarks on subsequent trouble-shooting expeditions. A slanting barrel brown with rust, a rectangular base-plate free from undergrowth, ammunition boxes, one with the lid open, and huddled alongside with their heads to the ground, three men. Or rather, three figures wearing faded battle dress and German helmets in dappled-white winter camouflage. The hand of the foremost figure rested on a rusty mortar bomb. A skeletal hand whose delicately articulated bones were still intact, it glimmered palely like the lower jaws that sagged beneath the helmets, forever robbed of the power of movement.

On they went, with the dark strip between no-man's-land and the Russian line on their left. A cluster of craters barred their path. The only means of crossing them was a tree that spanned the obstacle like a bridge. The sweetish stench pervading the forest had never left them, but here it was so intense that it took their breath away. The tree trunk was already trembling beneath their feet when they noticed the source of this stupefying miasma. Protruding from the waterlogged craters were legs, arms, ribs, skulls, tattered German and Russian uniforms. They crept on, lips compressed, faces streaming with sweat. Their backs ached and their eyes smarted from peering into the gloom.

A sudden hiss, and they were bathed in chalky radiance. A parachute flare had ignited overhead. Freeze, thought Quast, and automatically did as he'd been taught. Like four bizarre statues, they all stood stock still. The mist had lifted. Slowly, very slowly, the little white parachute drifted over them with its magnesium flare softly whistling and sizzling. Quast's eyes were glued to a tiny flower that had innocently, proudly taken root in the fork of a rotting branch. The flare landed, showered the motionless figures with four or five flickering, dying cascades of light, and went out. In the darkness that engulfed them, Quast groped for the frail little blossom and cupped it in the hollow of his hand. Then he pocketed it, carefully stowing it inside his cardboard spool of insulating tape. The Russian fire was still fierce but random.

The return trip seemed endless. In spite of Heberle's signalled appeals for caution, they relaxed. Ambling dreamily along, Quast almost blundered into a figure lodged in the coils of a rusty barbed wire entanglement with clumps of reeds growing through it. The man's trousers and boots were still padded out with what remained of his lower limbs. Above the waist, an olive-drab battle-dress blouse held the skeletal rib cage together. The curve of the bare skull glinted under a field service cap that had somehow defied the wind's attempts to dislodge it. Nasal cavity, eye sockets, and rows of teeth – one of them crowned with steel – combined to make a Halloween mask out of what had once been a human face. So urgent was the figure's pose, with arm outstretched towards the safety of the German line and rear leg trailing, that Quast was reminded of an action shot: a hurdler captured in full flight. The bullet must have caught him as he jumped, he thought with a shiver, and turned away. He saw Hapf cross himself, eyes wide with horror, and wondered if he'd done so earlier. Then he heard the click of a safety catch. Heberle called the password, and a sentry's face showed dimly through a cloud of mosquitoes, grey with fatigue. A section of birchwood palisade loomed up, and above it a screen of tangled vegetation. They climbed back into their own line.

Heberle spoke quietly with the No 2 Company platoon commander whom they'd just relieved of the need to risk his own men's lives by sending out a reconnaissance patrol. The order 'Resume firing!' was passed down the line. They ran the cable back to their dugout. Hassel came out to meet them, looked searchingly at Quast, and took possession of the cable drum, which was almost empty. By the time they were inside, leaden with fatigue, he'd connected the end of the cable to the receiver. Lieven adjusted the headset, switched on, pulled a message pad towards him, and started writing. He looked tense, and the tip of his tongue travelled slowly back and forth between his lips. They grinned at each other. Their trip had paid off: from now on, no Russian beyond that dark line of trees and undergrowth would be able to make a telephone call immune from surveillance and evaluation. When Heberle entered the dugout, he was met by the sound of laughter.

Quast learned his trade that summer. He could now locate a severed cable when the ends had been blown apart by a direct hit, repair one blind without making a sound, evade reconnaissance patrols, beat combat patrols back to his own line and raise the alarm. And all these things he could do even when suspense gripped him by the throat and olive-drab Russians slunk past only yards away.

They'd identified the numbers and coordinates of all the grid squares into which Russian gunners had divided the German positions. They knew the location of Russian artillery observers and listening posts. They knew when their enemy received his consignments of food and ammunition. They knew what it meant when a Russian operator said, 'Calling Beryoza: Four here for Sixteen. Pass the word to Fifty-two.' They were surprised to hear that the Russians were ordered to the rear for baths and physical training. They'd discovered why the enemy always started firing when a neighbouring company was relieved. They reported that enemy morale was low. The Russians' daily ration consisted of a pound and a half of bread, an ounce of sugar, three helpings of soup or gruel, and three quarters of an ounce of tobacco. The Russian salient was code-named *Koschkachikhvost*, or 'Cat's Tail', and the German salient *Chulen*, or 'Seal'. The enemy had women snipers, cooks, anti-aircraft gunners, medical orderlies, and doctors. The CO of the 1st Battalion had a thing going with a female medical officer of second lieutenant's rank named Lidya Vishnyakova, the CO of the 3rd with Olga Kamarova. The commmander of the Russian assault unit, Alexei Petrovich Petrov, enjoyed great popularity. The girl telephonist with the velvety voice was sleeping with him, much to the amusement of her fellow operators. Their ribald jokes made Sergeant Lieven lick his lips and snicker and slap his thigh so resoundingly that the others turned to stare at him, shaking their heads.

They'd learned a lot from their troubleshooting expeditions, which could number as many as four in a single night. Quast was inured to fatigue, stress, and suspense, to leaden limbs and lacerated hands, torn fingernails and bruised shins, smarting eyes and mist-blurred glasses. He knew how to husband his strength and respond to whispered instructions or premonitions of danger: 'Hey, there's something wrong up ahead' – 'Wait a minute!' – 'When I say move, move!' – 'Quick, into that shell hole!' He could recognize his comrades, even in semi-darkness, by their posture, gait, and laboured breathing. He had learned to suppress his distaste for wet rubber boots, the effluvia of mildew and damp wool, the oniony stench of clinging garments sodden with sweat, and the sour, acrid smell emitted by rotting vegetation. Tobacco smoke he liked, because it masked the cloying scent of putrid flesh.

One night, he stepped on an anti-personnel mine; it failed to explode. He dashed from one tree trunk to another, and a burst of tracer sped between his legs; not a scratch. A bullet severed a twig above his head; it missed him by inches. More and more convinced that nothing could happen to him, he moved about no-man's-land with the assurance of a lion tamer in a circus ring.

They spent most of one night laying a loop of brand-new cable in a neighbouring sector. Next day, they were informed that their services would be more valuable in the sector next door. Heberle refused to abandon the new cable, so they sneaked out into no-man's-land in broad daylight, along a stretch of dead ground. The gulley was a potential deathtrap, thick with mines and trip wires. To make matters worse, they had to crawl through a stream barricaded with barbed wire.

They started reeling in the cable, but Heberle was uneasy. 'Going to take a look,' he said. 'You carry on.' Quast saw him round a corner and dart back as if he'd been stung, heard him whisper, 'Listening post ten yards ahead, plus telephone! They spotted me. There'll be hell to pay in a minute – let's go!' Hapf cut the cable, Hassel slung the loose coils over his shoulder, and Sand grabbed the cable layer with the half-rewound drum. Heberle beckoned urgently to Quast, but some perverse kind of curiosity held him rooted to the spot. Seconds later he was crouching there alone beside Hassel's abandoned rifle and a litter of tools. He scooped everything up, stuffed Heberle's cap into his pocket, and made a dash for it. He was barely in the stream, with barbed wire plucking at his camouflage jacket, when a Russian mortar opened up. Splinters whistled overhead as he crawled on – gingerly, for fear of mines.

He made it at last and rolled over the parapet. The others were crouching in its lee, still out of breath. Quast returned Heberle's cap, propped Hassel's rifle against the wickerwork revetment, emptied his pockets of tools, and wiped his brow. The sergeant gave him an approving nod. 'Well,' he told the others, 'panic wasn't part of the exercise, but at least you all know what it's like now.' Then he turned to Quast. 'Incidentally, Signaller Quast, when I say withdraw, I mean it.'

They exchanged sheepish looks, then burst into sudden, relieved laughter and slapped Quast on the back. 'Man, are you a cool customer!' someone said, but Quast couldn't understand what all the fuss was about.

Not long after this, he was bold enough to question Heberle about his escapade in the Russian girl's hut. The sergeant took his curiosity in good part.

'Sonny,' he said, 'when two people are crazy to get together, you've no idea the lengths they'll go to.'

'Maybe,' said Quast, 'but the girl was Russian. Anyway, it's against regulations.'

'So what? She was a girl, wasn't she? As for regulations, they're dreamed up by armchair soldiers – they don't have any bearing on real life.' Heberle picked a beech leaf. He smoothed it out on his knee and looked at Quast. 'What do you want to do, divide girls into two categories, authorized and off-limits? Anyone who lets someone else dictate his likes and dislikes is a pretty poor fish.' He flicked the beech leaf into a puddle and stood up. 'You'll figure that out for yourself sooner or later. All right, go and see if we've got enough carbide for the lamp.'

8

AUTHOR: *Didn't your conscience ever prick you when you pulled the trigger on someone?*

QUAST: *I hate to have to say it, but the answer's no. It was like a game. We all stood the same chance and ran the same risks. Besides, I felt I was killing in a good cause.*

AUTHOR: *You think killing can be justified?*

QUAST: *I did then.*

Quast was nowhere near as imperturbable as he seemed. It was the sniper incident that first brought this home to him. He and Heberle were sitting outside the bunker one morning because the day already promised to be warm. A sedge warbler was trilling, and a whinchat proclaimed its presence with an intermittent 'tu-tic-tic'. Innocent bird-song, a gentle breeze, a soft blue sky, greenery that mantled the tormented forest like a gossamer veil, lethargy induced by many nights of nerve-racking vigilance, the comfortable certainty that their missions had been planned and carried out as duty demanded – all these conspired to lull them into a dangerously relaxed mood which isolated shots did nothing to dispel.

Then a runner appeared on their right, bending low. 'They've blown a gap in the screen,' he reported. 'Ten yards back – keep your heads down if you go that way.'

They nodded lazily and continued to drowse until they heard footsteps approaching from the left. It was a sentry going on watch – a weary, round-shouldered private with his rifle slung and his helmet on the back of his head.

'Hey,' they called, 'there's a gap in the screen ten yards on. Careful how you go.'

The soldier paused and looked at them stolidly. 'Oh, screw that,' he said and plodded off. Ten seconds later a shot rang out. They heard a groan and a thud, jumped to their feet, and saw it all: the sea of blood, the unnatural angle of the head, the whitish mass of brain tissue oozing down a tree trunk. Quast felt sick. Heberle patted him on the arm and drew him away.

The same night, Quast returned from troubleshooting with Hassel. Hassel crawled into his bunk right away, but Quast couldn't sleep. He suddenly saw the soldier again and heard his banal farewell to life. Only the violence and ferocity of his feelings inhibited him from bursting into tears. Corporal Michel, who was ensconced in the firing position beside the dugout with his rubber boots submerged and an MG34 ready to hand, complete with plenty of ammunition, saw him standing in the doorway and sensed his mood.

'Psst!' he hissed. 'Feel like giving 'em a belt?'

Quast settled himself behind the gun and nestled the butt against his shoulder. He pulled the bolt lever back and gently returned it.

'There's a machine-gun nest on the left, somewhere beside that marshy patch,' Michel whispered. 'It's been peppering us all night.' He smiled in the darkness. 'I don't think the bastard likes us.'

Quast selected automatic fire and took aim through the brushwood screen. Then he squeezed the trigger, releasing his pent-up anger in a way that owed nothing to reason or calm deliberation. The muzzle flickered and a stench of hot oil and spent explosive filled his nostrils. From beside the patch of swamp across the way, a cry of pain and fury rent the night. Michel slapped him excitedly on the back. A drumming sound came from the enemy line: wood on wood – Ivan's alarm signal. Flares went up and footsteps pounded along the Russian communication trench.

Michel jerked a thumb over his shoulder and whispered, 'On your way, hot shot!'

Quast dived back down the steps. The Russians had started to blaze away. Sand, who was standing in the entrance well, calmly took a drag at the cigarette cupped in his hand. Quast brushed past him. The oily black swamp water beneath his bunk sloshed to and fro as he climbed aboard. Hans, the Volga German interpreter, turned to look at him in the chalky lamplight, adjusted his headset, and gave him a nod. Dog-tired all of a sudden, Quast lay back and instantly fell asleep. He remained so until Heberle shook him awake.

'No 1 Loop's a goner. Hurry up, I want you back before first light!'

Within minutes, still bed-warm, he and Hapf were climbing over the parapet into no-man's-land.

A few days later they enlarged their area of operations. They were now manning two listening posts. One was sited right up front on the so-called Hammerhead, where a railroad embankment jutted into no-man's-land between two geographical formations code-named Half Moon and Magic Garden. This dugout was dry and sandy but so shallow that they could only move around inside with their heads down. The other was a thousand yards away in grass- and scrub-covered moorland, opposite Mouth Wood and its three clumps of trees: Beard, Jawbone, and Moustache. The path that skirted it, stretches of which were duckboarded and raised on piles, formed a link between the Germans' first and second lines of defence. Trying to put himself in the place of an enemy observer, Quast decided that the bulge of the dugout roof and the rusting T34 tank beside it could hardly fail to attract attention. He hoped they'd have plotted the Russian artillery observer's position and identified all his grid squares by the time the bombardment began. That, at least, would reduce the element of surprise.

Quast was always glad of a chance to leave the dugout,

which lay in the open moorland like a plum ripe for plucking. He was glad now, as he made his way to the Hammerhead with a message form. Having delivered it, he lingered on the expanse of sand that ran along the embankment for about fifty yards from the command post, flanked by barbed wire entanglements with narrow gaps in them. An NCO was handing out mail at one of the dugout entrances. The men who'd been waiting for news from home drifted off, some disappointed because their names had not been called, others happy to have received a parcel or a letter on drab wartime paper. Quast had been lucky. So had two corporals, who invited him to join them on a makeshift bench and share his tidings from the distant world called home. Just behind them was a sand-bagged sentry post. For some reason, Quast was attracted by its privacy. Why? It was dark and cramped, but he went in just the same. He leaned against the breastwork. A split second later he was deafened by the roar of exploding mortar bombs. The blast hurled him sideways and took his breath away. Dense clouds of sand choked and blinded him. Then came a scream so piercing that it constricted his stomach. He straightened up and dashed outside. There, in a welter of blood, lay the two corporals whose bench he might have been sharing. One of them, with his chest and hip torn open, was motionless. The other was doubled up and moaning, his face grey. 'Mother of God,' he said feebly, 'Mary, Mother of God . . .'

A soldier came running up. 'Do something!' Quast shouted. 'Get a medic!' But the soldier, who had knelt beside the moaning form, looked up and shook his head. The man in the sand moved his lips, silently now, and his face acquired a strange transparency. From one moment to the next, his eyes became gelatinous. The contorted body relaxed.

The kneeling soldier fumbled in the dead man's breast pocket and removed his papers. Two photographs fluttered to the ground at Quast's feet. The first was a family group: a young man in a sports shirt, a plump, fair-haired, laughing woman, and two little girls aged four or five, one with a ball in the crook of her dimpled arm and the other bending over a wickerwork baby buggy. The second showed a young woman with dark braids. Her sultry smile was half lascivious, half scared. There was a crocheted cloth on the table beneath her splayed thighs. She'd hitched her skirt up, and her stockings had slid down, concertina fashion, on to her shabby shoes.

Impassively, the kneeling soldier took the girl's photo and tore it up. Quast studied the dead man's face with dismay. Had his plump wife seen him as a hero? His wanton girl friend as an ardent lover whose every whim she gladly indulged? His children as a devoted father? Quast heaved a sigh. Wife, girl friend, children – he'd left them all behind forever. Someone covered the corpse with a shelter half. A yellow hand with bluish nails protruded. On it, a rivulet of blood was congealing among the dust that had settled there when the fountains of debris subsided. Quast's letter was still in his hand. He glanced at it abstractedly. 'We all hope you're in the pink,' he read. 'By this time, you surely realize how much better it was to become a signaller instead of an infantryman, right up there in the front line . . .'

He made his way back to the moorland dugout. Not that he noticed it, the sun was hot. Once inside the cramped wooden box, he crawled into his bunk and lay staring up at the roof timbers. Why had he taken his letter into the gloomy little sentry post? He couldn't account for it. Then his musings were interrupted by a sudden exclamation from Hans, the taciturn Volga German with the fair hair and broad cheekbones. He sat up with a start.

'They're targeting on our grid square!' Hans said excitedly, and proceeded to translate what he was hearing. '*Vnimanye, ogon!* Ready, fire!'

They strained their ears. Two reports, one fainter than the other.

Hans said, 'They're using two guns of different calibre, so our sound-ranging teams can't plot their position . . .'

Then came a whistling crescendo. Shells ripped into the marsh, some fifty yards short. Duds, thought Quast, until two muffled explosions betrayed the use of delayed-action fuses.

'It's us they're after,' Heberle said calmly. 'They're trying to crack us open.'

Hans, looking deathly pale, continued to translate. '*Vosyemdesyat metrov* – up eighty metres!' Again two distant reports, and again two shell bursts, this time fifty yards beyond them.

'They're bracketing us,' said Heberle, as calmly as before.

Hans was trembling now. '*Pyatdesyat metrov*,' he said in a hoarse voice. 'Down fifty metres. *Sorok* – forty metres right!'

They fired again. The shells whistled overhead and thudded into the ground, then burst. An outside splinter whirred through the air like a propeller.

Heberle said, 'That Russian observer needs his eyes tested.'

'Forty metres left!' called Hans. His voice broke. With a sudden sob, he flung the headset down on the table and dashed to the door. 'Stay here; you'll run straight into it!' yelled Heberle, but Hans, an ex-Red Army man who remembered all too vividly what it was like to endure a hail of German shells, tugged at the door. It had jammed. From outside came another sibilant crescendo, then two gigantic thuds and a double detonation. The bunker lurched and its vodka-bottle windows blew in. The men were thrown around like dice in a shaker. Hans dived out the door. They heard him panting as he raced up the steps.

Lieven, who had donned the headset, repeated the Russian artillery observer's words. '*Khorosho*. That's good enough. On target.'

Heberle scrambled to his feet and shouted, 'Fetch him back!'

Hassel was already out the door. Quast extricated himself from the ruins of his bunk. The two-tiered framework had collapsed. Lieven was recording the Russians' conversation on a message pad. Hapf retrieved his rifle from the dust and started to clean it. Suppressed excitement reigned. Looking at each other, they could read the same thought in every face. The Russians were preparing for a general assault – it could only be a matter of days. Everything added up: the unfamiliar accents of the new telephonists and officers on the other side, the new switchboards, the new code words. There was much talk of *utyugi*, or flatirons, *karandashi*, pencils, and *vyodra v dorogiye,* 'buckets on the way'. A prisoner had revealed that 'pencils' meant submachine guns. At night, the throb of powerful engines came from beyond Mouth Wood. Tanks? Gun tractors? And now the new batteries were ranging on the German lines – their own position included, as they had just discovered. Although they maintained a nightly watch for developments in no-man's-land, their latest troubleshooting trips had disclosed nothing more informative than numerous footprints and swaths of flattened grass.

They'd been drawing attention to these signs of activity for days. Russian telephone conversations were recorded on the right of their report forms, their own conclusions on the left. Every report in the past few days had ended with the words: 'Everything indicates that enemy forces are massing in this sector. Presume an attack in preparation. Signed: Heberle, Sergeant.'

9

AUTHOR: *What about comradeship? Wasn't it an over-rated word?*

QUAST: *I'm sure it counted for a lot, not just with me but with most of us. We even extended it to include the Russians. Like us, they were living under abnormal conditions. They felt much as we did and underwent the same experiences. It was only a short step from 'kill thy neighbour' to 'love thy neighbour.'*

The harassing fire, German and Russian, was heavier than usual. Tension hung in the air. That evening, Heberle had been summoned yet again by the senior divisional intelligence officer. 'See you tomorrow morning,' were his parting words to the detachment. 'And make sure you stay on your toes. Night, all.' The door slammed. Heberle's boots splashed through the seepage in the sunken entrance, padded up the steps, and receded. Silence fell.

Bored and dispirited, Quast threw himself down on his bunk and fell asleep. He had a dream. A fair-haired girl was standing in front of him. She had no skirt on, and her rounded thighs were smooth and white. She started to remove her blouse, but the sleeve came off in her hand with the arm still inside it. It looked strangely contorted, and blood was trickling over the back of the hand. Quast was knee-deep in glutinous mud. He tried to launch himself at the girl, only to see that her eyes were dull and her lips as white as snow. She was saying something, but what? He couldn't distinguish the words. Then he did.

'Hey,' she was saying, 'wake up! You've got to take this report back.'

He wrenched his eyelids apart and groped for his glasses. Sand was standing over him with a butt in the corner of his mouth. Quast downed a mug of stale coffee and unenthusiastically munched a crust of bread. He couldn't get the dream out of his mind. It was hot and stuffy in the dugout. There was no wind, and everything seemed uncannily quiet after the disturbances of the night. Sporadic rifle fire could be heard, but that was all. He still felt dog-tired.

He picked up the canvas dispatch case and reached for his rifle and helmet, then changed his mind. Rifle and helmet were regulation equipment for runners, but what was the point? A helmet only made you sweat, and why cart a rifle around when all you needed to carry was a sheaf of paper? Still fuddled with sleep, Quast made his way under the camouflage nets of the nearby antitank-gun emplacement like a daydreaming schoolboy. The sector was strangely peaceful. Mud sucked loudly at his boots as he plodded through it. He vaulted a dud half buried in the root of a tree – a swine of an ultra-heavy 12-cm mortar bomb.

A mud-encrusted motorbike was standing at the edge of the corduroy road. It belonged to a dispatch rider from corps headquarters. Quast looked round for him without success. Too bad, he thought. He'd have liked to hear the latest news, if any. When he reached the battalion command post, the CO emerged with shaving cream on his weather-beaten face. Quast saluted, but his ritual report was cut short by a brusque 'About time, too!' The major must be in a filthy temper, Quast told himself – he was a good ten minutes early. Taking the sheaf of closely written message forms, the CO turned on his heel and disappeared into the bunker.

Quast strolled through the pine trees to see how work was progressing on the intercept detachment's reserve dugout, which was to provide two dry bunks and room enough for batteries, cable drums, and tools. A couple of men from the signal company were busy roofing it with balks of timber. They were pleased to see him and welcomed the excuse to stop work. When they deviously angled for his help, Quast surprised them by stripping off his camouflage jacket and joining in eagerly. He was in no hurry to go traipsing back through the airless swamp, but he soon had cause to regret his decision. While hauling a beam out of a swamped and abandoned dugout, he trod on an iron cramp buried in the ground. One of the points pierced the sole of his right boot, passed between his toes, and emerged from the upper. Instantly, the boot filled with water. He swore. The day had started on a sour note, and now this had to happen. God alone knew when he'd get a replacement.

At that moment the Russians fired a light antitank gun. The crisp, incisive report had a whiplash quality that identified it as a captured German 3.7. Quast straightened up and grabbed his camouflage jacket. 'It's starting!' he said aloud. He'd never felt surer of anything in his life. Calling to the other two to take cover in the nearest dugout, he headed for it at a gallop. They stared at him incredulously. Then, with a roar like the jaws of hell opening, the horizon erupted. There was a concerted hiss, at once strident and hollow, as though a thousand giant fists were descending with superhuman force. Tensely, not daring to breathe, they buried their faces and fingers in the quaking mud. The barrage had begun.

Their temporary refuge belonged to the company runners' squad, whose members were earnestly seated around the bunker's shaking walls with helmets on, belts buckled, and rifles between their knees. Conversation was impossible. Barely a word penetrated the uproar, and near misses repeatedly drove the breath from their lungs. Their fluttering eardrums just picked up a faint cry for help in the distance: 'Stretcher! Stretcher . . .'

Half an hour went by, and still the Russian fire showed no signs of easing. A young runner jumped up, trembling from head to foot, and crawled under the table, where he cowered with his hands clasped over his ears. The squad commander, a corporal, patted him consolingly on the helmet. Rivulets of sand trickled between the roof timbers, and the bunker door shuddered as if someone were raining kicks against it from outside. Then it burst open. The adjutant's grim face loomed through a cloud of dust. 'No 2 runner, quick!' he shouted. Everyone looked at the figure under the table; it was the youngster's turn. The corporal stood up, a burly man with hands like shovels, a sandpaper complexion, and deep furrows between his long nose and the corners of his granite mouth. Quast knew him: he'd swapped his bread ration for Quast's cigarettes a few days before. He prodded the boy gently with his boot and shouted back, 'Coming Lieutenant!' As he lumbered out, Quast saw that sweat had painted a map on the broad back of his camouflage jacket.

Real guts, thought Quast. A farmhand and assistant tractor driver from some village in the Pomeranian backwoods, sallying forth into an inferno when he didn't have to . . . Then a runner dashed in and flopped down on the bench. Panting hard, he unbuttoned his jacket, the sleeves of which were torn, like his trousers. He was streaked with sweat and grime. 'The Ivans have punched a hole in the 10th,' he gasped. 'They're in the woods already.' The others looked up. 'Getting close,' growled one of them.

Fear seized Quast for the first time. He had no gun. What would happen if the Russians broke through in earnest? He was so preoccupied with the problem of how to get hold of a rifle that the crash of heavy shells exploding and the banshee wail of 'Stalin organs' – multiple rocket launchers – ceased to impinge on his consciousness. What scared him more than anything, as it so often did from then on, was a feeling of total ignorance. What was happening where? Decisive battle or local engagement? To the men on the ground, it made no difference. When the shit started flying, they were in the thick of it but out of the picture.

Uneasily, he rose and leaned against the bunker wall. Then the door burst open and another grimy figure stumbled in.

'There you are!' It was Heberle, shouting at the top of his voice. 'The 10th is under pressure. So's the Hammerhead – I'm going up there now. Get back to Regiment and tell Zastrow we're pulling out temporarily. Division'll have my balls for breakfast if we drag our feet and lose those LE40s. Once you get back, stay there.'

'Can't I come with you?' Quast shouted back.

'Do as you're damn well told, Quast. You're a signaller, not a rifleman!'

'Yes, Sergeant.'

'All right, move!'

Quast sprinted off. Heberle waved to him and disappeared into a pall of smoke, bound for the Hammerhead. Wherever it was visible between fountains of debris, the area defied recognition: paths buried, fresh craters filling with water, bunkers disinterred and upended. Quast knew a detour through the marsh. As far as he could see, the timber staging was intact. Three feet clear of the ooze, it swayed in the blast from innumerable shell bursts. Rifle bullets cleft the turbulent air and whistled through the sedge. Quast found himself alone outside the dugout, at the point where the path veered off on to firmer though still spongy ground. The roof had been partly stove in by a direct hit. Wondering if anyone could be inside, he squeezed through the lopsided doorframe. The place was in chaos. Debris, articles of clothing, underwear, a mess kit in a pool of coffee, but no sign of life. A rifle was lying on one of the bunks with some ammunition pouches beside it. He took them, glanced round the murky interior, and stuffed a pineapple grenade into his pocket.

Five minutes later, he reached the corduroy road. Fresh holes had been ripped in its timbered surface. Branches, splinters, and clods of earth hissed through clouds of grey dust. He progressed at a steady trot. On either side of the track, riflemen were crouching in full combat order with a scattering of noncoms among them. A lieutenant came running down the line, gesticulating. From the movement of his lips, Quast deduced that he was shouting orders. Evidently, the reserves had arrived. A shell blew a stack of timber apart. Logs whistled round Quast's ears. He threw himself flat. An empty cart rumbled past. He wondered why the driver was sitting on his box instead of running alongside so as to take cover more quickly. The vegetation on the left of the track receded to form a clearing. Spellbound, he came to a halt. So *that* was what a battery looked like in action: orange muzzle flashes stabbing the smoke-laden air, gunners with their shirt sleeves rolled up moving like robots, gun commanders standing erect. The steeply angled barrels recoiled and slid forward, recoiled and slid forward on their cradles with the regularity of pistons in an engine room. Just short of the clearing, the Russian barrage had transformed the forest into a solid wall of smoke and flame, but stray shells were sending up fountains of earth around the guns as well. Some of the artillerymen had torn uniforms, others were untidily bandaged. One of them fell on his face. Medics darted forward and carried him into a hollow. Quast stood there transfixed, craning his neck and staring.

An elbow dug him in the ribs. 'Are you crazy?' It was a rifleman. He shook his head and walked slowly on, unable to tear his eyes away. Ten yards along the track he came to the cart that had overtaken him. The driver was squirming on the ground with a gash in his thigh. Quast pulled out his first-aid pack. Far too thin. He plugged the wound with some gauze and bandaged it. Another rifleman, looking like a carnival figure with one side of his face stippled blue by powder burns, knelt down beside him.

'Got to fetch some ammunition,' groaned the driver.

'Grab hold!' the rifleman shouted to Quast.

They lifted the driver on to the cart and laid him flat. The rifleman thrust the reins into his hands. 'Good luck,' he said, and gave the horse a kick. The shaggy beast took fright and galloped off in the direction of regimental headquarters.

With a gesture of farewell, the rifleman disappeared down a barely discernible path through the greenery bordering the track. Quast walked on, feeling as if his journey would never end. Though sparser, the shell bursts were just as violent. He staggered under their turbulence. At last he reached a bend. Another shell brought a tree crashing down on the track ahead of him. And suddenly, compared to the pandemonium that had just been raging around him, it was quiet. He turned to look. The barrage might have been drawn with a ruler. Two or three hundred yards behind him billowed a curtain of debris, black and yellow smoke, and dirty white vapour.

Captain Zastrow acknowledged his report with a nod and ordered him into the blockhouse beside his command post. Quast tottered into the log cabin, which was half embedded in sand. Though tight-chested with suspense and exhaustion, he felt happy to have done what was expected of him. Now he deserved a rest. He slumped on to a bench. The other occupants of the blockhouse were rear-echelon personnel. He shook his head in answer to their questions and shut his eyes. A sudden shout jolted him awake.

'Zastrow wants the man from the intercept detachment!'

Quast struggled to his feet and stumbled outside. Zastrow was beckoning to him from the entrance of the command-post dugout. He had a message form in his hand.

'Know how to get to the Hammerhead, even if the Russians have cut the road?'

'Yes, Captain, I know a way round.'

'Good, I want you up there at once. Your detachment is to fall back on the 10th, but you've got to keep operating from the Hammerhead at all costs. We need your reports more than ever now.'

Quast saluted and said, 'Yes, Captain.' That's all I needed, he thought, and trotted off. Five minutes later he was facing the curtain of fire. He jammed his cap down on his head, quickened his pace, and disappeared into the smoke.

Counter-attacks were in progress, but none of the men he passed – wounded, runners, ammunition carriers – could tell him how close the Russians were or in what strength. He was glad when a runner fell into step beside him. A rifleman was lying under cover near the path with his back to them.

'Watch out,' he called, 'the Ivans are somewhere up ahead!'

They flipped their safety catches, ready to fire from the hip. Hearing a rattle and click on their left, they dived for cover and nervously pumped a few shots into the under-growth, then stumbled on at a crouching run. They were eventually hailed by a German sentry concealed behind a tree stump, facing in their direction.

'Any Ivans still around?'

'Search me!'

Quast and the runner nodded good-bye and went their separate ways. Quast was now on familiar ground, with the Hammerhead immediately ahead. Here, too, the scenery had changed. There were fresh craters every-where, stretches of hurriedly erected barbed wire, mounds of damp, crumbly soil. The dugout was heavily barricaded. The loops had been blown to pieces, but so-called earth spikes had already been screwed into the ground to enable enemy telephone traffic to be picked up at short range. Scraps of conversation gleaned by Sergeant Lieven indicated that the Russians were in chaos and trying to regroup. 'No 9 Rifle Company wiped out . . . Colonel Kosiyev of the 177th instructs you as follows . . . Where is Lieutenant Lebedev of the submachine-gun company? Any news of Captain Nazarov? I saw Sergeant Balakov blown off the parapet. By the time we got in among the Fritzes, half the platoon was missing . . .'

Quast delivered his message. Heberle, who cocked an eyebrow at the sight of him, said, 'What, you back here?' Hassel hugged Quast and drew him aside into an empty firing position. 'They say the Ivans'll be kicking off again any time. Let's stick together from now on.' He produced a bottle of Steinhäger from a waterlogged ammunition box. One swig was enough to fill them with childish insouciance. 'Hey, Ivan,' they called into no-man's-land, 'come over here! *Na zdorovye!*' Heberle frowned at them and mutely shook his head. Not a shot broke the silence.

Going outside, Quast abruptly sobered up. Opposite the dugout entrance, a tree stump jutted knee-high from the mud. A ration carrier – an uncouth, stupid-looking private – dumped an ammunition box on it and opened the lid. The zinc-lined interior was full of melting margarine rations and slices of pink sausage as thick as a thumb. 'Three helpings each,' the ration carrier sang out. 'There's more than enough to go round now.' Quast felt half sickened, half angry, but not just because the man's unappetizing invitation was a callous reference to the losses they'd sustained in the past few hours. Barely a yard from the tree stump sprawled a body in Russian uniform. It belonged to a member of the assault company that had made it across the corduroy road before being cut down by murderous defensive fire. German infantrymen had raked them from foxholes and dugouts driven into the reverse slope of the embankment.

Quast slowly replaced the slice of sausage he had just picked up and stared, open-mouthed, at the Russian. He was a young man with a profile as pretty as a girl's. His close-cropped fair hair was caked with blood, his nostrils were translucent, and his eyes stared blankly into an evening sky like a mauve sea dotted with islands of crimson cloud. Slender, boyish fingers still gripped the rifle, with its coarse-grained wooden butt. A beetle was cautiously traversing one waxen ear. The lips looked bluish against the alabaster face, and the upper lip was slightly retracted. Quast could sense the boy's wild élan as he charged across the road, his pride at being among the first to reach the German position, his shock at being suddenly exposed, with a handful of others, to bursts of fire from all sides, his last-minute realization that the end had come. Quast saw himself lying there. The Russian looked as if he might have gone to school with him, played in the same basketball team. Uniforms apart, he could see no fundamental difference between them.

Grief and rage welled up inside him as he returned to the dugout. Seated with his back to the wall, tight-lipped and silent, he began to wonder if he hadn't been thinking along the wrong lines all the time. That young Russian was far closer to him than the hawk-nosed colonel, far less alien than assholes like Lieutenant Ellberg and Sergeant Major Briegel. The human barriers that really mattered weren't lines of battle; they followed quite another route.

Then he looked across at Heberle, who was bending over the map with the interpreters, and all at once it struck him: Heberle was his friend. He'd sent him back to get him out of the firing line. 'Don't be so goddamned inquisitive,' Heberle had told him not long before. 'Don't go crawling through every minefield and stretch of barbed wire you see.' Then, after a pause, 'A few of us better get back home when this is over, Quast. There'll have to be some changes made, if you know what I mean.'

A few days later they were sitting in the dugout with their hair combed, their uniforms brushed, and their rubber boots washed. 'Make sure you talk sense,' Heberle told Sand. 'And you, Hapf, don't stand there with your

mouth open if he asks you a question – he won't bite you.'
He walked to the door just as Zastrow entered and stood aside.

'The General!'

'Atten – *shun!*' barked Heberle.

They jumped up and stood as erect as the headroom allowed. Even before Heberle could report them present or accounted for, they heard the general say quiety, 'Sit down, everyone, you'll crick your necks.' He was a handsome man with greying hair – careworn and paternal-looking, thought Quast, who was impressed by the decorative effect of his Knight's Cross. The general propped his walking stick against the table and looked at Heberle.

'Sergeant Heberle, by awarding you the Iron Cross First Class, I'm honouring your entire detachment. You and your men have done a fine job. That's what I came to tell you all.'

He leaned across and pinned the decoration on Heberle's chest. Zastrow put a bottle of brandy on the table. 'Mugs!' Heberle told Hassel out of the corner of his mouth. They all clinked mugs with the general, whose Knight's Cross bobbed every time he moved. Quast was in a festive mood.

Outside, a thin drizzle was falling. So were a few Russian shells. The general had a word with each of them. Education, civilian occupation, front-line experience – a real man-to-man talk. When told that Quast was a high school graduate, he said, 'Like to try for a commission, Signaller?'

'Not any more, General.'

'Why not?'

'It's all I can do to take care of myself when things get rough, but looking after a hundred men or more – I don't think I'd ever get a wink of sleep. As for taking responsibility for orders from up top, General, I – I simply couldn't do it.'

Everyone stiffened – nobody moved a muscle. A shell splinter smacked into the breastwork. Quast looked around, momentarily at a loss.

The general regarded him gravely. 'You don't know how right you are,' he said quietly. 'Come and see me when you're back at Division – all right, Signaller Quast?'

'Certainly, General.'

They rose and bumped their heads against the dugout roof as the general took his leave. Once the door had closed behind him, Heberle was engulfed in laughter and congratulations. An hour later, while changing for another foray into no-man's-land, Quast came to a conclusion: there was a real possibility that the general had sympathized with his inability to grasp, even now, how the military machine could grind on regardless of the still-warm bodies of men killed minutes before. Fetching rations, replenishing stocks of ammunition, posting sentries, improving defences – no matter what happened, the wheels continued to turn.

10

AUTHOR: *That Russian girl could have been a partisan. Aren't you ashamed of having kissed her?*

QUAST: *Why ashamed? We were just a couple of kids.*

AUTHOR: *What about Russian women in general? How did you rate them?*

QUAST: *If Germans of the older generation have anything in the way of a soft spot for the Russians, in spite of all they've done to each other, the credit certainly doesn't belong to Lenin. Russian women are immensely warmhearted . . .*

Quast was disappointed when Heberle's detachment was withdrawn from the front line. He'd grown genuinely acclimatized to their Hammerhead position. Besides, a spell in reserve meant a reunion with Sergeant Major Briegel, and that could only spell trouble.

To begin with, all went well. Sergeant Max draped an arm round his shoulders and called him 'our pocket Napoleon', and the rest of Max's signallers gave him a warm welcome. Then he went back on guard. This time, Briegel dispensed with pretexts: he simply detailed Quast for guard duty. Hassel suffered the same fate. In Briegel's book, they were still replacements.

Quast had sores on his feet after wearing wet rubber boots for so long. The sores turned septic and refused to heal in the heavy leather clodhoppers they wore behind the lines, so he took them off whenever he could. That made him late for muster. The remainder of the company had already fallen in by the time he limped to his place in the ranks. Facing the parade with his legs planted firmly apart, the sergeant major treated him to a scathing reception.

'Ah, nice of Signaller Quast to join us. Now he's had a whiff of gunsmoke, he thinks he can take it easy.' Briegel couldn't forgive Quast for having seen him hit the dirt – and for being a high school graduate, or so he'd heard. 'Maybe you'd care to tell us why you're late on parade?'

'The Sergeant Major got it right first time: too much gunsmoke.'

'Are you shell-shocked or something?'

'Shell-shocked? Not me, Sergeant Major.'

'In that case, Signaller Quast, you can sort your ideas out on guard duty.'

'Of course, Sergeant Major.'

'Say "yes", when you acknowledge an order!'

'Yes, Sergeant Major.'

Tiring of Briegel's blatant self-importance, the rest of the company started to shuffle their feet in a hostile way.

The sergeant major's voice turned falsetto with fury. 'What's the matter with you all, feeling your oats?'

'No, Sergeant Major, feeling sick,' Hassel replied between his teeth. He clapped a hand over his mouth.

Briegel was nonplussed. 'What!'

'I'm going to vomit any minute,' gurgled Hassel.

'Then, fall out, you miserable streak of piss!'

Hassel doubled off behind the nearest hut. Once out of Briegel's range of vision, he leaned nonchantly against the wall and gave Quast a cheerful wave. Meanwhile, the sergeant major was reading out orders and rosters in a wrathful monotone. Hassel reported back, looking suitably woebegone, and rejoined the ranks under Briegel's withering gaze. Excitement ebbed. Then Briegel called for two volunteers to test a new radio set under combat conditions. The words were hardly out of his mouth when Quast and Hassel stepped forward. With three weeks to go before their next scheduled spell in a listening post, they could bank on getting back in good time. Briegel darkly made a note of their names. Heberle looked dubious at first, then grinned at them. If they stayed with the company much longer, disaster seemed certain. It would be better this way.

A little later, peals of laughter issued from the intercept detachment's billet, a simple peasant hut between the road and the edge of the forest. Sand was mimicking Quast. 'Shell-shocked? Not me, Sergeant Major!' he crowed, slapping his thigh. Maria, the thirty-year-old widow whose home they temporarily occupied was weeping softly. One of her children was in beleaguered Leningrad; the other, like her husband had been killed during the German advance. '*Voina nix khorosho,*' she sobbed, 'war no good. Why you have to march again, my little student? Here, let me look your clothes.' And she checked, for the umpteenth time, to see if the buttons on Quast's shirt needed reinforcing. 'She's mothering you again,' said Heberle, grinning broadly. Maria thumped him on the chest and called him 'great big idiot'. Sand rose with a flourish, picked up the cookhouse loaf he had swapped for his cigarette ration, and headed for the door. 'I need a woman,' be announced. 'Horny brute,' Hapf said disgustedly, and Heberle, wagging his head, called after him, 'Why don't you tie a knot in it?'

The village boasted one woman of easy virtue – the only really fat Russian girl Quast had seen there. Well, he reflected, at least Sand had hit on one way of anaesthetizing himself against the malaise that overcame them all from time to time: the feeling that some time soon, maybe today, they'd vanish without a trace like spit on a stove. Life would go on without them, yet they'd never really have lived. When the moment came, they wouldn't even know what they were leaving behind.

It was dark outside the cottage. On impulse, Quast went out and loitered there in the hope of seeing Tonya, who called him *chort* – 'devil' – and told him she detested all Germans but waited for him when he asked her to. They'd exchanged a few bashful kisses and engaged in some mild petting. Quast, who didn't really know what to do with Tonya, felt ashamed of his inexperience. She regarded him with warm, sad eyes, took the glasses out of his hand – he'd removed them because they got in the way when he kissed her – and put them back on his nose. 'Silly little German,' she whispered. Then, laughingly, she tweaked his ear and ran off.

There was no time to dwell on Tonya next day, which was swelteringly hot. He had the new walkie-talkie – known as a G Pack – strapped to his back, his headset on, and the hand controls clipped to his belt. A few hundred yards down the track, seated in a cart driven by a pipe-chewing auxiliary and drawn by a nag that snorted at every step, Hassel was likewise wearing earphones and twiddling knobs. Testing the new sets now would be better than making a hash of things in action.

They spent the night under canvas in a transit camp. What with the rumble of gunfire in the distance, the clatter of carts, the roar of trucks and jeeps, the words of command, the shouts of 'Heave!' from men unloading supplies, and the steady tramp of marching feet – some bound for the front and others for the rear – it was a noisy, restless night. It didn't get dark properly, either, little more than four hundred miles from the Arctic Circle, so their 4 A.M. start came as something of a relief.

A thin mist swathed the forest. Grasshoppers, reed warblers, and tree pipits were already trilling, twittering, and carolling, and draughts of chill dawn air refreshed their lungs. Before long, the picture became more familiar. It wasn't as deceptively peaceful any more. Corduroy roads, splintered trees, ambulances – Quast began to feel at home again. Beside them, with its barrel at forty degrees, a howitzer bellowed at the sky. Though startled and deafened, they laughed: it was the kind of music they knew.

By way of a sandy ravine, they reached the regimental command post, which lay in an expanse of scrubland pockmarked with shell holes. Zastrow greeted them inside the bunker.

'So you thought we couldn't win the war without you, eh?'

They grinned at him, then listened intently as he briefed them. He was attaching them to the 1st Battalion. After running preliminary tests near Battalion Headquarters, one of them would be sent up front, first to No 9 Company, then to No 10. The other would set up a station at Battalion and establish a radio link. 'You're just in time,' Zastrow concluded with a faint smile. 'There's trouble brewing all along the line.'

Their hands were halfway to their caps when he stopped them in mid salute. 'One more thing, gentlemen: no heroics. You're simply here to test an item of equipment. I don't want those gadgets falling into enemy hands; is that clear?'

Squeezing through the bunker's narrow entrance, they were confronted by two prisoners awaiting interrogation in a recess at the foot of the steps. The encounter was so sudden that they broke into disconcerted laughter. The Russians shyly joined in, and their air of apprehension faded. The four young men stood face to face, two close-cropped and two shaven-headed, two in camouflage jackets and two in olive-drab blouses. Common to them all were the clear eyes and coltish movements of youth.

Zastrow, who was peering up from below, broke the spell. 'Hey, this isn't a kindergarten. The war's not over yet, boys. Get to work – and you two Ivans, come here. *Idi syuda! Davai, davai!*'

Quast and Hassel re-emerged into the light of day. They had arrived on the scene of the third battle of Lake Ladoga.

The hills, none of them more than a hundred and fifty feet high, consisted of fine sand ranging in colour from white to yellowish grey. The pines on them, many of which were still intact, had gnarled red trunks glistening with beads of resin. Bordering the ravines and defiles were tousled fir trees interspersed with birch saplings. Peaty water glinted in the midst of marshy brown and ochre patches, and from them sprouted drab green tufts of sedge and clumps of windswept reeds. Quast was reminded of the Brandenburg moors.

They breasted a rise. Ignoring their guide's warning against Russian shelling, they paused to look. The plain's sandy ridges dissolved into a buttermilk haze that merged with the dark green horizon. The battle lines were scarcely discernible in the shell-scarred expanse below. A parachute was billowing like a spinnaker from the stump of a lone, decapitated tree. Quast could see no sign of the aircraft it had come from. They crossed a dip, ascended another gentle incline, and reached the battalion command post, which was dug into the slope. Once there, they jettisoned their equipment and looked at each other. Hassel said, 'Loser stays here at Battalion.' Then, so that each stood an equal chance, they played the stone-scissors-paper game to settle who did what. Their guide shook his head and vanished into the dugout, where they heard him announce the arrival of two 'crazy men' who'd come to try out some radio sets.

One A.M. Pandemonium reigned throughout the sector. Quast was installed in one corner of the dugout behind a blanket curtain, listening to Hassel's voice over the G Pack. It was distorted but loud. A combat patrol had been repulsed and a prisoner was already on his way to the rear. The company had sustained two casualties, one of them fatal: a platoon sergeant. More field dressings were needed. Periodically, since they were there to test the sets, they switched to Morse. Comments on the G Pack's performance they enciphered; only messages relating to current operations could be sent in clear. Quast was working by the dim light of a Hindenburg candle. Russian planes traversed the sector all night long, the drone of their engines alternately swelling and fading. The ground shuddered under their bombs. The Russians' ground–air radio traffic sometimes came through so strongly that Quast and Hassel had to stop sending. Outside, a voice called, 'Watch out; phosphorus bombs!'

Hassel had just sent 'QRX 10', meaning break for ten minutes. Quast removed his headset and went outside. The ground was churned up. Embedded in the sand in front of him lay a phosphorus bomb – a dud. Behind the lines, a German night fighter was hammering away at a heavy Russian bomber homeward bound after raiding supply routes. Quast saw tracer, saw flame spurt from one of the bomber's engines, saw the whole plane convert itself into a gigantic fireball.

The bombing slackened as dawn approached. The Russian artillery fell silent too. Quast and Hassel decided to sign off and take a nap. Quast fell asleep over his G Pack.

Towards midday, he learned the meaning of air superiority. There were no German planes to be seen. Instead, the sector was attacked by five Russian fighters – ponderous-looking, heavily armoured Shturmoviks whose engines emitted a sinister scream each time they banked away. Still drugged with sleep, Quast tood fright because he thought they had designs on the command post, but the sturdy single-engined fighters pulled up, banked steeply to the left, and raced towards an emplacement housing six 20-mm light anti-aircraft guns.

He didn't know whom to admire most: the pilots heading straight into a hail of fire at thirty feet, or the gunners serving their pom-poms with parade-ground precision. Again and again the Shturmoviks came curving in, each plane spewing fire and metal from its twin cannons and machine guns. Bombs rained down. The anti-aircraft guns fell silent in turn. One toppled on to its side, with the bodies of its crew draped over it. Another jammed, to judge by the frantic movements of the men who were wrestling with it. In the end, only two guns were still answering back. The Shturmoviks came in for another pass, even lower this time. The gunners concentrated on the two leading planes. A plume of black smoke trailed from the second. The pom-poms tracked them, pointing at the sky until their gunners were nearly supine, then swiftly traversed and swung down to pump streams of tracer at their receding targets. The Russians screamed away, almost into a quarter roll, and streaked off low across the plain. One fighter was coughing and the plume of smoke from the other had become tinged with flame. The Soviet star on its fuselage gleamed blood-red. The deadly birds vanished into the haze. A blackish-yellow pall of smoke hung over the gun emplacement.

Hassel turned up, sweat-stained and grimy after suviving a near miss. While he was patting the dust off himself, they discussed technical problems and decided to swap duties at daybreak in future, because that was when the shelling was least intense.

Quast went forward with a runner. The shellfire was so heavy that he couldn't get his bearings. He kept his eyes fixed on the runner's back as they blundered along at a crouching run, throwing themselves flat or sprinting across stretches of open ground. At last he was seated in front of the G Pack, sweating like a horse. The dugout was dry and well built. It had no light shafts but plenty of headroom. By local standards, enemy fire in this company sector was normal: fluctuating small-arms fire, periodic mortar attacks, sporadic concentrations of shellfire. Radio traffic was brisk: reinforcements on their way, an antitank gun to be dug in, additional supplies of hand grenades being sent by Battalion.

Standing in the trench outside, Quast saw flares hiss into the sky from both sides of the front line. Waist-high in a recess beside him stood a tiny, 5-cm mortar – a so-called

112

Hitler Youth cannon – complete with a box of bombs. Anyone threading his way along the trench dropped one down the spout as a matter of routine. Peace descended with the approach of day. Hassel, who turned up at nine, announced his intention of grabbing a couple of hours' sleep. Quast shouldered his pack and rifle. 'Give my regards to the Ivans if they come,' he said. 'See you tomorrow morning.'

Next day, just as he was about to go up front, all hell broke loose. The shellfire grew heavier by the minute, rising to hurricane pitch. At 6 A.M. Hassel's voice came through the headset. 'Enemy advancing on a broad front!' There was a swift alternation of attack and counter-attack. They had to switch to Morse because the roar of exploding shells drowned their voices. Quast was installed in a small dugout on the reverse slope of the nearest bridge. The battalion commander came in and patted him on the shoulder. Hassel radioed: 'SOT – changing position. EB 15 – wait fifteen minutes.' Quast went outside. The air reeked of explosive. Nearby were some short-barrelled, beefy-looking IGs, or infantry-support guns. The crews were tensely dragging at their cigarettes: still no order to open fire. Quast threw himself down behind the ridge and looked to his left. He gave a horrified start. Down there in the Barskoye Plain, only a few hundred yards away, olive-drab figures were swarming across the shell-pitted ground: Russians. Damnation, he thought, if they veer left . . .

He backed off fast, heading for the radio, and bumped into an officer – a replacement who'd exchanged a few words with him when reporting his arrival to Battalion Headquarters. Now the new boy was standing there with his helmet askew and his hands fluttering, tears streaming down his ashen cheeks.

'N-no reserves left,' he stammered. 'W-what am I supposed to do? The C.O.'s up front.'

Quast could see that his nerves were shot. 'But,

113

Lieutenant,' he said, 'we've still got the IGs. They're stuck here doing nothing. Why not turn them loose?'

The lieutenant stood there without moving. He stared for a moment, then remembered. 'But of course, the IGs!' Pulling himself together, he turned on his heel and yelled at the platoon commander. 'Get those guns into position and prepare to open fire – hurry!'

By the time Quast had his headset on again, the mortars were in place behind the ridge. Targets, angles of elevation, and fuse settings ran out, and bomb after bomb came speeding from the stubby barrels. The air was thick with smoke. Quast clamped the earphones to his head.

'Enemy breakthrough on left,' Hassel reported. 'They're swapping grenades at fifteen yards.' Quast bit his lips and uttered a silent prayer that Hassel would make it. Then the headphones started cheeping urgenty. 'QQQ – interrupting transmission. Will explain later.'

Quast packed up. He'd decided to move to his reserve position at Battalion Headquarters. If Hassel got through again, he could just as well pass the information to an officer or runner there, and if the Russians came over the ridge it would be better if they only caught a glimpse of his G-pack. The door creaked open to reveal a mud-covered rifleman with his helmet on the back of his head and an 08 in his hand. He flopped down on the bench and said hoarsely, 'Give us a smoke.'

Quast produced one from his haversack. 'Where are you from?' he asked.

'No 9 Company,' said the rifleman. 'Is there a dressing station around?'

'Yes, behind Battalion HQ. Why?'

'Got a jab in the back. Lucky I had this' – the rifleman weighed the 08 in his hand – 'when the Ivans jumped us. Then the next wave arrived . . .'

Quast inspected the damage. A gaping stab-wound, raw red flesh, the whole back glistening with blood. 'And you sit here smoking?' he said.

'Why, is this a nonsmoker?'

'Christ, get going before you pass out!'

'I'm on my way.' The door slammed shut.

Holding the G Pack like a briefcase, Quast emerged from the dugout. The ridge and the IGs behind it were now attracting heavy fire. The new lieutenant was lying stiff and motionless with his legs half buried and his face in the sand. The crumpled map beneath his left hand displayed jagged holes and crimson splashes. A runner followed at Quast's heels. Halfway down the slope, something exploded behind them with a terrible roar and a blinding flash. Quast fell headlong, didn't move. Pain? Blood? Neck? Shoulder? His back was on fire. The runner picked himself up off the sand and groped for his helmet. Blood was trickling out of his ear. He shook himself and felt his head. 'That was close,' he said. Quast indicated his back. The runner gave his jacket a perfunctory tug. 'Nice clean tear,' he said. 'And there's a hole in your hide.' Quast worked his shoulder blades up and down and felt a pinprick of discomfort. They grinned at each other.

Quast set up station a hundred yards on, in the bed of a stream. He sent his call sign but Hassel didn't reply. Although the air was thick with smoke, the shellfire was gradually decreasing. He sat in the open with his back against a dugout wall to be sure of seeing Hassel if he came over the ridge, but Hassel didn't show. Straggling columns of riflemen carrying stretchers loomed out of the dust. The soldiers stumbled along in their tattered, grimy uniforms, some of them bandaged. Groans came from the men on the stretchers. A stump of an arm swathed in dirty, bloodstained gauze pointed at the sky. More and more uneasy, Quast questioned all comers. 'Seen Signaller Hassel? Attached to No 10 Company?' But the men shook their heads or ignored him, mute with fatigue.

Then he was hailed by a runner. 'Signaller Quast?

You're wanted back at Regimental Reserve right away!'
Gathering up his rifle, haversack, and radio, Quast set off.
He felt dejected. If Hassel had bought it, his G Pack could
go to hell. When he reached the string of dugouts near the
regimental command post, Heberle materialized in front
of him like a genie.

'What brings you here, Sergeant?'

'Don't get fresh with me, Signaller Quast.' Then, after a
pause, 'Man, am I glad to see you in one piece!'

'Don't forget the precious radio set, Sergeant.'

Heberle dug him in the ribs. 'The hell with that.
Where's Hassel?'

'No idea. The last thing he sent was a triple Q.'

'Shit! Oh well, you'd better go and see what's up.'

They were hardly inside the dugout when Quast was
called to the phone. It was Lieutenant Strehling, No 2
Company commander. 'I've just been on to Regiment,
Quast. I'd no idea you were such an ace radio operator.'

'Me neither, Lieutenant.'

'Is the G Pack any good?'

'You bet. They've finally produced a box of tricks that's
up to date, not like the Mark D. It's foolproof – a real
winner.'

'Glad to hear it. Listen, Quast, Army's forming an
assault battalion – a brand-new outfit with a fabulous
range of equipment: automatic rifles, G Packs, quadruple
pom-poms, MG42s, a howitzer battery of its very own . . .
How would you like to join it?'

'I wouldn't, Lieutenant. I feel at home in your outfit,
now I'm not a humble replacement any more. I'd never
volunteer for a transfer, not now.'

'But I can't promote you inside the company – there
are dozens of men ahead of you. You still want to be a
signaller three years from now? That'd be a waste of
natural talent. How about it?'

'The answer's still no, Lieutenant.'

'Don't talk bullshit, Quast! You're volunteering for the

116

Assault Battalion – I've already put your name down.
You couldn't do better if you tried. And now, get straight
back to company headquarters. You're moving out
tonight.'

11

AUTHOR: *The general seems to have made quite an impression on you.*

QUAST: *Yes, meeting him made me realize how stupid all the conventional clichés are. I'm glad he didn't end up on a meathook in Plötzensee Prison.*

AUTHOR: *But he did send soldiers to their deaths, didn't he?*

QUAST: *Sure he did. Men died for no good reason on his orders, but once he grasped the truth he atoned for their deaths by dying himself. Compared to the self-righteous cant of people who've never had to face such ordeals, there's greatness in an act like that.*

Though taken aback, Heberle was determined not to let Quast see it. Strehling was the only officer in the signal company he really had time for, and now it was Strehling who proposed to rob his intercept detachment – his well-drilled team – of a valued member. Heberle's face mirrored this conflict between pride in his own command, concern for Quast's advancement, and respect for Strehling. Then the telephone buzzed again.

'Lieutenant Schuster's on his way to you with the new call sign and frequency schedules.'

'If it isn't one thing, it's another,' growled Heberle, but Schuster failed to show up. Heberle called Regiment and was told that the lieutenant had left over half an hour before. 'Unless he's strayed into the Russian lines,' said

Heberle, 'something must have happened to him.' He alerted some engineer reserves, who spread out five yards apart and made their way towards the regimental command post.

Russian mortars were maintaining a desultory fire. They had to take cover from time to time. On one such occasion, when Quast was hugging the sand, he looked up and saw Schuster just ahead of him. The missing lieutenant was flat on his back in a shallow cable trench with a briefcase on his chest. His face was waxen. To judge by the moistness of the earth in the shallow, circular crater beside the body, he'd been dead for only ten or fifteen minutes. There were deep wounds in Schuster's neck and back – vicious, lethal wounds inflicted by mortar-bomb splinters.

Silently, they carried him down to the corduroy track, where Heberle summoned a jeep from company headquarters. 'Better take him along,' said Heberle. 'Lend a hand.' Heberle, Quast, and the driver bent Schuster into a sitting position and manhandled him into the rear seat, beneath the canvas top. Heberle turned to Quast. 'You sit beside him. We'll drop you at Division. The general wants to discuss the war with you.' Heberle joined the driver in front. Quast didn't listen to what they were saying. He sat as still as possible, making himself as small as possible, beside the dead lieutenant who'd preached the virtues of duty and patriotism with such fervour six months earlier, and who now preserved such a grisly silence.

They passed the captured howitzer, which greeted them with an earsplitting roar. Some MPs waved them down. 'Papers?' barked one of them. Heberle merely jerked a thumb over his shoulder. The MP saw the lieutenant's shoulder straps and put a hand to his helmet, then looked again and lowered it. 'Drive on,' he said in a subdued voice.

They really did stop at divisional headquarters, even though Quast thought Heberle had been joking. The farmhouse kitchen was dimly lit. Quast lined up with two sergeants and a corporal. An ADC inspected their uniforms and wrinkled his nose at the rents and mud stains. 'Oh, well,' he said at length, and withdrew.

The general turned up ten minutes later. It was clear, as he inserted the ribbon of the Iron Cross in Quast's buttonhole, that he remembered him perfectly. 'Show as much courage as you've shown in the intercept detachment, Quast,' he said, 'and you won't go far wrong. Courage is a fine thing, but remember: courage plus conscience is worth even more. You understand?'

Quast, who didn't understand, quickly forgot him. The next time he heard of him was during the aftermath of 20 July 1944. Apparently, the general had died after being hunted and gunned down by the Gestapo. Before he expired, they operated on him without anaesthetic and artificially stimulated his circulation to enable them to question him. Those who had sheltered him while on the run were hanged. Those who had denounced him, a young civil engineer and his wife, received a reward of five thousand marks.

That evening, Quast was relieved to hear that Hassel had made it back to the regimental command post unscathed, but he couldn't wait for him. He formally reported his departure. Heberle gripped his hand hard and wished him luck. Strehling slapped him on the back and told him to spare an occasional thought for his old company. He gave Sergeant Major Briegel an impeccable salute. Then he marched out into the night.

Even before he could make the acquaintance of his fellow sufferers in the Assault Battalion, an orderly-room clerk discovered that Quast was overdue for leave. Within hours, he had boarded a train for Germany. Autumn was approaching, and mist hung in the air. Whenever they halted, sentries had to jump down on to the ballast and patrol each side of the train – closely, to prevent partisans from attaching mines or limpet bombs to the coaches.

A sergeant told Quast what he had heard at army group headquarters. It was estimated that by the end of December the partisans would have launched their ten-thousandth sabotage attack on the railroad network that was so vital to the flow of supplies and reinforcements. Ten thousand attacks in a single year!

'You see?' said the sergeant. 'Up front – that's the safest place to be.' Quast thought the sergeant must be pulling his leg. According to him, three hundred locomotives and over eight hundred items of rolling stock would be derailed, smashed, or reduced to scrap by the end of the year, and thousands of men had already been killed or wounded in transit.

Somewhere up ahead in the mist and darkness, the locomotive gave a strident whistle. The sentries hauled themselves on to the footboards as the long train moved off with a jerk. Quast was standing in the corridor. He'd finished his spell of guard duty and was in no hurry to return to the muggy compartment with its aroma of stale sweat, tobacco smoke, cheese, and schnapps. Leaning against the window beside him was a stocky woman with the collar of her black leather coat turned up. Mid thirties, short dark hair, nondescript face. A big Alsatian was nestling against her thigh. Quast didn't venture to pet it.

'What are you two doing here?' he asked.

The dog growled. 'Been on detachment,' the woman said curtly. 'Going back on duty.'

'Where are you stationed?'

'Ravensbrück Concentration Camp.'

'You don't say! I've always wanted to know what goes on in those places.'

Scrutinizing him closely, the woman sensed how artless the implied question was. She said, 'There's nothing much to tell. It's a labour camp for female prisoners. Politically unreliable types, Marxist agitators, enemies of the state,

121

riffraff, social misfits – that kind of person. We keep their noses to the grindstone.' She paused. The roar and rattle of the train rose to a new pitch, and the gaps between the rails jolted their knees. 'You're doing your patriotic duty out here. We can't have people stabbing you in the back, can we? They've got to work – pull their weight. Our boys at the front need all the help and support they can get; don't you agree?'

'Of course,' said Quast. 'I can see that, but it doesn't sound like much fun.'

'Fun?' she said. 'Don't tell me you're having fun out here.'

Conversation lapsed. The Alsatian panted loudly. Gloomy tracts of Russian forest slid past the window.

There was the apartment house his parents had moved to. Red brick, narrow windows, arid-looking shrubs in the communal garden. His father was bound to be away. After her initial surprise, his mother would take his presence for granted. Her boy was having a hard time; it was only fair of them to let him off the leash sometimes.

But it wasn't his mother who opened the brown-painted door of the apartment. Facing him in the dimly-lit hallway was a dark-haired woman of about thirty. Her raincoat and suitcase indicated that she'd been on the point of going out. She eyed him curiously, this youngster from another planet with his fresh face and weary eyes.

'I'm the lodger,' she said. 'You must be the son of the house. Your mother won't be long. How was your journey? I'm due at the station, but I've still got a few minutes to spare.' She put her suitcase down and let the raincoat slip off her shoulders. 'Where are you living – I mean, whereabouts in Russia are you serving?'

Her voice trailed away. Quast, who had been staring at her all the time, propped his pack and rifle against the wall without taking his eyes off her. He pushed the door to and came closer. Amused at first, then gravely, she returned the gaze that conveyed such a world of innocence and curiosity, such a desperate craving for affection.

Quast took the woman in his arms – thrust his body against hers and kissed her passionately, dazed by his own impetuosity. He muttered something unintelligible. 'You poor boy,' she whispered. Then she kissed him back as no girl had ever done. He felt drunk. Take her into the bedroom, he told himself. Hold her tight – do it, do it now!

Footsteps padded along the corridor and keys jingled. They released each other. The woman stepped back quickly and tidied her hair in the mirror. Quast stood there with his arms hanging limp, still dazed. The footsteps receded, but the spell was broken.

'I'll only just make my train,' the woman blurted out.

He gazed at her imploringly. 'When do you get back?'

'Two weeks.'

'But I'll be gone by then.'

She shrugged and drew a deep breath. All at once, he felt infinitely remote from the corpse-infested forests of Russia, from shellfire, radio sets, and intercept receivers. He only knew he'd never see this woman again. Disconsolately, he held the door for her. She smiled at him and said softly, 'My name's Vera, by the way. Enjoy your leave.' He felt forlorn when the door closed behind her.

The more often Quast came up against illogicalities in what he was doing, the more firmly he clung to the ideals that enabled him to accept them. Everything at the front was governed by military necessity, by rules and regulations. Do your duty, he told himself; others are there to perceive the grand design behind it. He put aside dreams, whims, fancies, and emotional subtleties in the belief that it was natural to serve the Fatherland, whose needs were all that lent meaning to this renunciation. For such a cause, he was ready to shoulder any burden. Discounting the malcontents and hypocrites among them, those of his comrades who bothered to look for a meaning came to the same conclusion.

But now he was at home, and what he saw there didn't tally with his preconceived ideas. It came as a shock. He'd set out on the journey like a child returning from boarding school to the familiarity of his parental home, but that had been a mistake. Home? There was nothing homely about this appalling mediocrity, this drab Philistinism. Cardboard window-panes, ration cards, housewives haggling over bacon and eggs, obituary notices adorned with Iron Crosses and insincere tributes to the dead, blustering propaganda, meaningless claptrap in the press, a convulsive lust for life that hid the fear beneath – no, the Fatherland of his dreams looked altogether different.

So he didn't enjoy his leave, after all. He slept, ate, evaded his mother's loving, foolish questions, and endured the neighbours' admiration. If he heard a sudden hiss while crossing the street, he flinched and prepared to throw himself flat. He stiffened at every unexpected noise. Social chitchat left him cold. The movies he saw with his mother seemed ludicrous. The newreels showed nothing but victories and represented the war as a grand opera. He dipped listlessly into books he had devoured with relish only a short time before. They now meant nothing to him.

He was sitting in the garden, under a sun devoid of warmth, when a slim, fair-haired girl came over – Rosemarie. Rather shyly, she said hello and sat down beside him.

He knew what was going on: His mother had told everyone around that her boy was in need of distraction. Quast was offhand, unfriendly, and unfair. Rosemarie was all the things a girl of her age ought to be – pretty, intelligent, amusing, vivacious – but her efforts were wasted. When she showed an interest in his doings and tried to draw him out, all she got were noncommittal answers. Quast was indifferent to her silky hair, dainty little

124

breasts, and long legs. He had a letter in his pocket. Alfons Hassel was dead -- killed by a direct hit from an antitank shell on the parapet he'd been climbing over into no-man's-land.

He couldn't reveal, even to his father, who interrupted an official trip to catch a glimpse of him, how unhappy he was – how close he felt to everything out there and how remote from his family.

In 1933 his father had expatiated on Germany's national resurgence. Before long, a National Socialist swastika replaced the Nationalist Party's colours in the flag-holder on the living-room balcony. What a mercy, his father had declared: six million jobless off the streets, a real army again, a younger generation taught to appreciate the virtues of fresh air and the fact that men's hands were made for rifles and grenades as well as cigarettes and glasses of schnapps . . . But now, when his father looked at him, Quast thought he detected something akin to doubt, guilt, fear, and concern for the son whose life and future had taken such an unwanted turn.

They bade each other a noisy, nonchalant farewell, like two old cronies, but only to hide their own forebodings.

After a few days, Quast told his mother he was going to Vienna to see Margot, who had since been bombed out of her Berlin home. Frau Quest raised no objection. Although she didn't understand him, she was ready to defend his decision to anyone who even hinted that it mightn't be essential to desert her so soon.

Standing outside the ornate door of the imposing Viennese mansion, he suddenly wondered what he was expecting. Did he really think they'd welcome him like a prodigal son?

Eberhard' mother opened the door and stared at him coolly. 'Yes, what can I do for you?'

'Had he really changed so much?

Margot appeared in the elegant hallway behind her. She

recognized him but didn't feign delight at seeing him again.

'Eberhard's missing in the Crimea,' she said without preamble. Then: 'Do come in.'

Quast played the old soldier. He said it meant nothing that Eberhard had been posted missing, because chaos always reigned in combat areas. New units were formed, old ones disbanded, batches of mail lost, names mixed up . . . It sounded thoroughly unconvincing.

He was invited to supper – a gloomy occasion. Eberhard's mother was drawn and haggard with worry, Margot abstracted and only superficially friendly. They didn't question him about his own experiences or hero-worship him, for which he was duly grateful. He hadn't the courage to tell Margot that she was the sole reason for his presence in Vienna.

An hour later, he was making his way through darkened streets. The sidewalk resounded under his hobnailed boots. People hurried past, muffled up against the icy wind. The avenues were flanked by handsome but forbidding stone façades. At the hostel for combat personnel, a former barracks, Quast was allotted a plank bed covered with grey woollen blankets. There was no one around except a stoop-shouldered corporal reservist who handed him a towel and showed him the way to the showers. There must have been a hundred empty beds in the old barrack room, whose windows had been painted over as an air-raid precaution. Quast chose one in the farthest corner. He propped his rifle at the head of the bed and deposited his pack and boots beside it. His uniform he draped over a chair. Padding to the door in his socks, he turned the clumsy, old-fashioned light switch. The emergency lighting was a feeble glow. He groped his way back to the wooden box, with its lumpy mattress and concave bolster, and crawled between the blankets. He thought of Eberhard, Hassel, and Vera, and took comfort in the fact that he'd soon be rejoining the Assault Battalion.

* * *

The hospital train was bound for the front. The beds were already resplendent in virgin white sheets, and seated on one of them, next to a sliding door, was Quast. He'd been attached to the escort responsible for guarding the train during its trip through partisan-infested territory. Now it was standing in the midst of a white plain swept by ceaseless flurries of snow. If the blizzard hadn't revealed a few huddled shacks, some crumbling masonry, and the timber staging of a water tower, no one would have guessed that this was a station.

Powder snow was sluggishly melting on the window. Quast stared out. A ghostly, white-encrusted locomotive came panting up behind the train. There was a hiss from the safety valve, a clank of worn-out piston rods. They were condemned to an hour's wait at least.

For several seconds, the curtain of snow parted to reveal the dim, squat shape of a church in the background. 'Good God,' Quast said aloud – the Almighty actually maintained a command post in this wilderness. Minutes later, with his overcoat collar turned up, he was trudging across the tracks and into the blizzard, heading for the church. When he reached it, he found the door locked. Some rusty oil drums were stacked beside it, their ugliness mitigated by drifts of snow. Quast looked up at the walls, saw fissures in the flaking, off-white plaster, saw the bulge of the onion dome against a matt white sky from which the sun's milky disk had long since disappeared. It was growing dark.

He wondered what the church had been since the Revolution. A forge? A fuel depot? A factory? Perhaps the interior still retained some shred of its former dignity. Perhaps he would be stirred by some residue of what had once inspired solemnity in those who crossed its threshold. He toiled through the drifts creeping up its walls and tried to dislodge the planks nailed over the east door, but to no avail.

When he was back in the empty coach and blowing on

his frozen fingers, he asked himself what he'd hoped to achieve. Had he hoped to recapture the sweet sense of bliss that encased him like a cocoon when he trotted off to Sunday school with a catechism in his hand? Or the organ whose thunder drowned the shuffling feet and creaking pews? Or the lilac scent of the Bible he'd closed with a petulant snap, vowing never to reopen it for all eternity?

Sunlight slanted down into the classroom, motes of dust dancing in its rays. Quast strove valiantly to be carried away by the magic of Bible stories, but he couldn't evade the details that made it so hard to accept them with simple faith. Why did Jesus always break bread – why not use a knife? Why did the disciples go to sleep instead of sitting up with him when he was in such a state? Why did they all desert him and run away? Why did he pick such lousy friends? Why did he give the blind their sight and then ask them not to mention it? Why had he said, 'He that hath ears to hear, let him hear'? Were many people born without ears in those days? Heinrich, Quast's next-door neighbour in class, was nudging him and whispering again: he wanted to play battleships.

Herr Herbst, the Scripture teacher, banged his desk with a ruler – this was the third time – and barked, 'Quiet back there!' But Heinrich took no notice. He continued to fidget and whisper, and that was what did it.

'You, come here!' Quast didn't budge – he thought Herbst meant Heinrich. 'Look sharp!' No, the words were directed at him. Bewildered, he jumped up and hurried to Herbst's desk. Why him?

'Quast, I forbade you to talk and you did.'

'I wasn't talking.'

'That's the last straw! You're not only disobedient, you're a liar as well.'

'I'm not disobedient and I'm not a liar!'

'I see, so you're insolent into the bargain!'

Quast was confronted by a salmon-pink face with

128

spiteful, bloodshot eyes and sandy lashes. He turned away in disgust. Herr Herbst had a wart in the corner of his mouth and a mesh of mauve veins on his nose. At ten inches' range, Quast could see his bristly nostrils and smell his fetid breath.

'Look me in the eye, Quast! You're disobedient, you're insolent, and you've lied to your teacher – in Scripture, too!' Herbst rose, a lean and lanky figure. His lips were twitching. 'Well, *that*'ll teach you what happens to pupils like you.' Quast's face took a slap from a bony hand with yellow fingernails and ginger fuzz on the back. 'And that, and that, and that!' Tears of impotent rage welled up as his head jerked to and fro. He stood there stiffly, uncomprehendingly, with his fists clenched.

The bell began to jangle in the corridor. Herbst lowered his hand. Quast's defiant 'Amen' was lost in a metallic clangour. He walked unsteadily back to his place. Taking his Bible, which was warm from the sun and gave off such a beguiling scent, he slammed it shut. 'Never again,' he muttered. After all, what sort of God would let a bully like Herbst represent him on earth? What sort of religion edified the helpless by permitting the mighty to slap them in the face?

Years later, Quast declined to attend confirmation classes. He never was confirmed, and his Hitler Youth platoon commander took pride in this youthful display of National Socialist intransigence.

The coach gave a violent lurch. The locomotive had taken its place at the head of the train. Steam came hissing through the heating system. Quast could smell the Bible's lilac scent as vividly as if it were lying open in front of him. He smiled. Five minutes later there was a penetrating smell of 'cow toothpaste', the army-issue cheese that came in a tube. Quast was spreading himself a slice of bread. Although he didn't like the yellow slime, he overcame his revulsion. The trudge through the snow had made him hungry. Chewing, he wondered where God really was – up at the front? If so, which side was he on? And if the answer was both sides, how did he contrive to be universally fair?

12

AUTHOR: *I believe you when you say you cherished a vision of the Fatherland, but what was really in your mind?*

QUAST: *That's easy. If you belong to a family that has suffered injustice and fallen on hard times, you do your best to improve its lot and restore its reputation. That's how I saw my relationship to the Fatherland. I was misinformed, at least partly, but my feelings were sincere enough. I felt a sense of responsibility – I thought it was up to me.*

What were Army HQ's plans for the Assault Battalion? Rather than rely on scuttlebutt, Quast consulted Werner, the orderly-room sergeant. He and Werner had argued at length over the relative merits of cigarettes and bread as practical aids to men in combat. Quast favoured an emergency supply of bread. He cut it into cubes and toasted them till they were crisp. When things got rough and ration carriers couldn't get through, he munched them slowly. Werner swore by the soothing and hunger-assuaging properties of deep lungfuls of tobacco smoke. Now he volunteered some inside information.

'I can tell you precisely what they aim to do with us,' he said. 'I've seen the order – it's top secret, naturally. The Assault Battalion comes directly under Army HQ from every angle. What's more – now get a load of this – we're the Army commander's last operational reserve for use in extreme emergencies, quote unquote. By the time they send us in, there'll be no one behind us and no one left in front of us but Ivans, get the picture? They're going to start by cutting our teeth on a couple of minor operations, just so we know where we stand.'

The Assault Battalion had been drawn up in an open-ended square, squad commanders on the right of their squads, platoon commanders on the right of their platoons, company commanders on the right of their companies, company sergeant majors on the left.

The day was grey and heavily overcast. Beyond an undulation in the featureless plain, which was covered in drab brown grass, could be seen the thatched roofs of a village and a delicate tracery of leafless birch trees. The battalion commander, Major Haldinger, completed his third tour of the ranks on a chestnut gelding. The general was expected any minute. Haldinger had posted a lookout at the end of the track to give warning of his approach. The horse snorted and tossed its head as Haldinger circled at a trot. The company commanders reported their strength. Quast tried to keep count but was distracted when one of the gelding's hind hoofs almost flattened his boot. He made the total seventeen officers, a hundred and twenty-seven NCOs, and seven hundred and thirty-eight men. He hadn't miscalculated after all: the adjutant called out the same figure.

Everything happened very quickly after that. Haldinger ordered all men with decorations into the front rank. 'Hurry up!' he shouted above the resulting turmoil. 'Makes more of a show,' he murmured to the adjutant. Then another refinement occurred to him. 'Shorten slings!' he ordered. They busied themselves with their rifles, tightening the slings till they lay flush with the stock. Moments later, a shot rang out and a bullet went whining into the air. A rifleman on Quast's left collapsed.

Haldinger trotted over and looked down at the crumpled figure. A sergeant materialized on the double. 'The man's dead, Major.' Haldinger digested this information

132

impassively. Just then, the lookout sprinted across from the end of the track. 'The general, sir!' Haldinger didn't hesitate. 'Get him out of sight!' Two men dumped the body behind a bush and doubled back to their places. The general appeared on a dapple-grey charger, followed by his entourage. Their horses' hoofs sent up showers of mud.

Haldinger saluted smartly. 'Assault Battalion – seventeen officers, one hundred and twenty-seven NCOs, and seven hundred and thirty-seven men – present, correct, and ready for inspection!'

Seven hundred and thirty-*seven* . . . Quast didn't know who impressed him more: the Army commander, aloof and unapproachable as Mars himself, or the poker-faced major who, within seconds of a fatal accident, had coolly deducted its victim from the tally of those who now stood stiffly at eyes right. They were lucky to have a CO like Haldinger, thought Quast. All the same, the Assault Battalion had suffered its first casualty even before its members had been kitted out or given a chance to become acquainted. Hardly a good omen . . .

It later transpired that a rifleman with a round in the chamber and his safety catch off had inadvertently pulled the trigger when shortening his sling. The bullet had passed through the head of the man in front of him.

The exercises designed to breed familiarity between the officers and men of the Assault Battalion were pure routine. They all knew their trade, though Quast continued to be puzzled by the transformation of inoffensive civilians into combat specialists with the sort of homicidal instincts he'd observed in himself and others. What helped to foster their fearsome proficiency in the art of killing?

For one thing, they drank together. To Quast, an ascetic by upbringing, their wild bouts of self-intoxication seemed weird. For days after the first such binge in the 'rats' nest' listening post, he'd stolen curious glances at

Heberle and the rest. Were these calm, well-disciplined men really identical with the drunks who'd so recently bellowed with inane laughter, wept floods of tears, sighed over family photos, indulged in crazy horseplay? Was it really he himself who'd sat there over a brimming mug of vodka, jabbed the back of his hand with a lighted cigarette, heard the sizzle of seared skin – and felt nothing?

One afternoon, Heberle had decreed, 'Orgy at 1800 hours. White tie and tails.' That meant wearing their camouflage jackets with the off-white winter side outermost. Cans of sardines were opened, loaves of bread and lumps of fat bacon sliced, and bottles of vodka blended with a special allocation of canned peaches to produce the diabolical beverage known as 'jungle juice'. There were two guests of honour. One was Corporal Michel, 'for having instructed Signaller Quast in the use of the MG34 with such outstanding success that he silenced a Russian machine-gun nest'. The other was a combat patrol commander from No 2 Company, 'for having stated that information compiled by the intercept detachment had saved the lives of at least two platoons'. Hassel was deputed to convey the invitations in person and recite them word for word.

Dusk was falling when they assembled in the dugout and opened the proceedings by knocking back a mug of vodka apiece. Later – much later – Heberle conducted a mock trial in which all were given parts to play. He himself acted as judge, Hassel and Sand as associate judges, Hapf as prosecuting counsel, the interpreters as witnesses, and the guests as spectators. The accused – Ivan – was absent, but his absence was excused, 'on account of exceptionally unfavourable geographical conditions'. He was represented by his court-appointed attorney, Quast.

Ivan was charged with deliberately spoiling their summer vacation outside Leningrad. He had prevented them from eating regular meals by firing off his guns with reckless abandon. He had kicked up a senseless din, thereby causing a breach of the peace. Last but not least, he had cunningly employed millions of Bolshevik mosquitoes to milk the vacationers of the world's most precious fluid: German blood.

The more they drank, the more preposterous became the arguments tossed back and forth, at the tops of their voices, by officers of the subterranean court. Quast's pleas on the Russians' behalf assumed a treasonable form. Spectators and associate judges nearly fell off their benches with rapturous laughter.

'Counsel for the prosecution,' Heberle roared at Hapf, 'unless you pull your socks up, I'll find Ivan not guilty and we'll all go home!'

'Good idea,' mumbled the second of their guests. 'Be honest, what the hell did we come here for in the first place?'

Sand enlightened him: 'The vodka, of course.'

Quast's next digression earned him a rebuke from the bench. 'Why bring Napoleon into it?' Heberle demanded. 'You're spouting enemy propaganda, you commissar, you!'

Yes,' Hassel said menacingly. 'What would the Führer think of you, Comrade Quastinov?'

'I don't see the Führer,' growled Michel. 'Did any of you see him? My guess is, he's gone looking for his war. He can't find the bloody thing in all this mud.'

'You mean he's *lost* it?' shouted Lieven.

'Blabbermouth! You said that, I didn't,' Michel shouted back. 'Boys, give old Lieven a drink while he's still got a head on his shoulders!'

Eventually, Heberle passed judgement. 'Our brother across the way is hereby sentenced to cease fire and hand over his female telephone operators – soonest!' He rose unsteadily to his feet and put his cap on with a series of grotesque contortions. 'What's more,' he added, 'I'm going to tell him so right now.' On that note, he tottered out the door.

It was Quast who broke the drunken, flabbergasted silence. 'Hey,' he said thickly, 'we'll lose him if we don't do something quick!' They trooped outside. Heberle had mounted the dugout roof and was standing there with his arms outflung, preparing to deliver a speech. Hassel and Quast pulled his legs out from under him. He slid into the entrance well like a sack of potatoes. While they were still blundering around in the narrow trench, roaring with laughter, at least three Russian machine guns opened up. 'You see?' cackled Heberle. 'Ivan's a spoilsport. *Nix kultura!'*

Two months later, Quast recalled, they'd been resting in their rear-echelon camp when an orderly arrived with an invitation from the officer's mess: Would Heberle attend a guest night? Heberle promptly declined – 'Either the whole detachment comes or nobody does!' – so they'd all been invited. They duly turned up in their winter camouflage and were greeted with a chorus of mocking allusions to angels in white.

Verbal skirmishes raged with the young second lieutenants, who were little older than Hassel or Quast and only a few months longer out of school. The MO told smutty stories and subsided into a flood of fond recollections. 'Candies,' he kept saying, ' – I stuffed them up her one by one and licked them out. Scrumptious!' He had a lisp.

Quast, who suddenly found the bedlam intolerable, went outside for a breath of air. A lieutenant was standing there buttoning his fly.

'Come to attention when you see a German officer!'

Quast obediently clicked his heels, reflecting that no two drunks acted alike. The lieutenant came so close that their chests were nearly touching: one child in uniform confronted another.

'High school graduate?'

'Yes, Lieutenant.'

'Why aren't you an officer?'

'Too smart, Lieutenant.'

'You're drunk.'

'Yes, Lieutenant.'

'What's the betting you'd keel over if I pushed you?'

'Not me, Lieutenant.' Quast withdrew one foot.

'Hey,' said the lieutenant, 'that's not fair. Your feet must form an angle of eighty degrees; the drill book says so.'

Quast replaced his foot. The lieutenant jabbed him in the chest with one finger. Quast fell flat on his back. Giggling insanely, the lieutenant watched him scramble to his feet.

'How do you plan to win the war, Signaller?' You can't even stand straight.'

'Standing straight won't do it, Lieutenant. Spend too much time at attention and you end up with your backbone sticking out of your ass.'

The lieutenant drew himself up. 'A German officer stands as straight as a German oak, Signaller!'

Quast said, 'One little shove, that's all.'

'Try it.'

'Is that an order?'

'It is!'

Quast shoved. The lieutenant fell over and scrabbled around like a pig in search of beechnuts. He sat up and bellowed, 'Know what you just did? You assaulted a superior officer!'

'Orders are sacred to me, Lieutenant.'

The lieutenant struggled for words. Then he relapsed into the mud and started snoring. Quast groped his way back into the dugout.

Four A.M. The alert came without prior warning. Although they grumbled, torpid with sleep, they loaded their arms and equipment in record time. An hour later they were heading for the front in a convoy of grey one-

137

and-a-half-tonners. Before long, columns of smoke and debris were springing up on either side of the road. The trucks disappeared into a dip flanked by fields of stubble. Then they made a sharp left-hand turn and swung round till each was facing the way it had come. The men piled out. Weapons and equipment were unloaded, emergency supplies of ammunition issued. Plumes of dust drifted past, mushrooms of smoke and fountains of earth erupted in their midst. In open order, with five yards separating each man from the next, they plodded towards the front while the trucks roared back down the road at full speed.

Quast heard Haldinger tell the signal-platoon commander, 'From tomorrow morning, I want Müller and Quast assigned to me.' He felt pleased. A tall, bony sergeant who looked after his men as a hen tends her chicks, Heinz Müller had been a farm manager in peacetime. He was shrewd and circumspect, with a sense of humour that often made him grin at Quast and curb his impatience. Whenever he spoke or laughed, his long nose twitched in such a comical way that the very sight of him was a boost to morale.

Their position – aptly code-named 'Arrow Salient' – was based on a railroad embankment projecting into enemy territory. The line crossed a sunken river-bed by way of a stone viaduct spanning the Kuzminka Gorge, and dug into the side of the gorge was the battalion command post. The signallers occupied a bunker in the embankment just above it.

The units holding Arrow Salient had so far managed to beat off Russian attacks and regain lost sections of trench, yard by yard, in fierce hand-to-hand fighting. They had almost drained their strength in the process, but the Russians were not expected to renew their attacks for at least twenty-four hours, because their own losses had been equally heavy. The Assault Battalion was inserted into the sector on the right of the embankment, code-named 'Right Arrow', so the under-strength companies in the trenches could close up. Müller pronounced their position the craziest and least favourable he'd ever seen, and he spoke with the authority of one who'd fought in France and Yugoslavia, in Sebastopol, the forests outside Gaitolovo, and the Pogostye pocket.

The CO swore roundly. Their ammunition convoy had been pinned down by heavy shellfire. 'We'll be in trouble if we don't get that stuff right away,' Quast heard him say. 'There's time, Major,' said the adjutant, but Haldinger was adamant. 'There isn't, I can feel it in my bones.'

That evening, the voltmeters on all their radios slumped to zero. The batteries supplied by Army were flat. No one could account for this phenomenon. Sabotage? Faulty charging? Quast was detailed to fetch some replacements from a supply depot. Dusk was falling, and the entire sector was being subjected to harassing fire. German gunners, too, were peppering enemy positions and assembly areas. Flares went up, flickered, and died. The air was dank. Quast shivered as he climbed into the cab of the truck. The driver, a taciturn Bavarian, had been instructed to collect some entrenching tools from the same source and return with Quast and his batteries. It took them an hour to reach their destination, a commandeered farmstead. Quast jumped down into the muddy, rutted road. It turned out that the supply depot had not been authorized to issue any batteries. Haldinger's written requisition had no effect. The technical sergeant in charge, who was wearing carpet slippers and had been asleep, to judge by his bleary, surly expression, greeted Quast in the depot office with his back to a notice board adorned with equipment inventories and a pin-up of Marika Rökk. He tried to shoo him out, but Quast stood his ground.

'Check it out. Call my CO, call the army signals chief, call the C in C – call anyone!'

'Why should I? I need those NC28s for my own outfit.'

'If I go back without any batteries and my CO fires off

a complaint to the general, Sergeant. I wouldn't like to be in your shoes.'

'Who's going to back your story up?'

'The driver – he's just coming. Anyway, I'm not leaving before you've signed a rejection slip.'

'And if I don't.'

'Then the driver'll be my witness.'

'I ought to kick your ass!'

'The most you can do is kiss it, Sergeant.'

Outside, a squeal of brakes announced that the truck had backed up to the loading ramp. The sergeant met Quast's stubborn gaze with a venomous glare. At length he shrugged and said, 'Have it your own way.'

The batteries he issued had been badly charged, but that they didn't discover till the next day.

13

AUTHOR: *Bloodshed and horror on the one hand,
Lena's animal health and vitality on the other . . .
Didn't it strike you then that love was more fun than
war?*

QUAST: *No, it never occurred to me, and I'm glad it
didn't. I'd have been so demoralized, I'd have gone
to pieces.*

It was 5 A.M. when Quast was finally able to stretch out on
a verminous bunk in the signallers' dugout. At 6 A.M.,
somebody shook him awake. Russian guns of every
calibre had been pasting Right Arrow and its lines of
communication for the past fifteen minutes, but Quast,
more comatose than asleep, had noticed nothing. Müller
hauled him into a sitting position and shouted, 'Shake a
leg! The Major wants us right away.' Quast struggled to
his feet and tottered over to get the radio, dazed and
deafened by the pandemonium outside.

Then the thunderbolt struck. The dugout wall caved in
with a rending crash. He was hurled to the ground. The
impact knocked his glasses off and dislodged one lens.
Blood started trickling from his nose. He groped for the
radio. The air was thick with dust. Someone beside him
whimpered for a medic, someone in a corner groaned
inarticulately. After a feverish search, he found his glasses
in the debris beneath him – he even salvaged the missing
lens, undamaged. Towing the radio after him, he crawled
outside on his hands and knees, Müller, who appeared out
of nowhere, knelt down and relieved him of the set. Then

141

they both went sliding down the side of the gorge to the command post. Haldinger clicked his tongue at them.

'Ah, so our gentlemen signallers have turned up at last. Don't strain yourselves, will you!' He wagged his head.

In other words, thought Quast, things were looking lousy. Haldinger couldn't issue any orders because he didn't know where the Russians would start the ball rolling. Worse still, there wasn't enough ammunition up front.

A few minutes later, Quast had No 1 Company on his headset. 'Where's that ammunition? They're concentrating their fire on the trenches.' Half an hour later: 'Enemy attacking . . . Enemy breaking through on right flank.' Later still: 'Break-through neutralized. Urgently require grenades and ammunition.' Quast replied, 'Two parties on the way.' The CO had patched them together out of walking wounded, clerks, and cookhouse personnel. Then came: 'Out of ammunition. Going in with the bayonet.' Contact was lost after that. The other companies' signals grew fainter too. Salvos of Russian shells and rockets were straddling the command post with undiminished ferocity. Quast couldn't distinguish a word. He lugged the set outside and threw himself flat on the slope near the entrance.

Flustered though he was, he found himself delivering a monologue. And now, he muttered – now you're going to set the frequency very slowly, very steadily, with the touch of a virtuoso. No matter if the ground heaves: you're just a pair of ears. No matter if sections of embankment come cascading down, or the stream peters out or duckboards go whirling through the air: You've got to find your people in this din, so press the headset to your ears till it hurts . . .

A Russian voice came through, preternaturally loud, then a beefy transmitter sending numbers in Russian, then a German operator cheeping out five-letter groups, then more Morse, some sent by a hesitant hand, some rattled off at twenty words per minute. Reception fluctuated, the signals alternately soaring to an unintelligible screech and fading until they resembled the flatulent bass of a giant tuba. Somewhere in this jungle of noise he'd find his opposite number. He had to pick out his own people – their lives might depend on it.

Another monologue: Pull yourself together, Quast. Be thankful you've no time to shit yourself . . . There they were at last – very faint: '. . . repulsed. Need·grenades, repeat, grenades. Rest of ammunition party arrived. Trenches held at half strength.' That was No 2 Company. Not a peep out of No 1.

The CO picked up his helmet and pistol. 'Come on, Hanke,' he called to a runner, 'we're off to No 1.' He turned to the signallers. 'No 3 Company command post – be there in thirty minutes.' Then, with the runner at his heels, he headed for No 1 Company.

When a rocket salvo slammed into the gorge on either side of Quast, the blast stunned him. He came to in a sort of limbo, deafened and almost unable to breathe. Müller dragged him into the dugout and looked at him anxiously. Quast shook his head. He was unscathed. So was the set, apart from some minor scratches, but the battery supply was failing fast. Hanke reappeared. 'Quick,' he said, 'the CO's up with No 3 already.' They packed up their gear and dived outside.

It had been freezing. Now it was thawing, and the ground was like soap. They staggered and slithered from one shell hole to the next. The firing had eased by the time they reached No 3 Company command post. Laid out in a row beside the dugout, ready for transportation to the rear, were a score of bodies. As always when he saw men lying so strangely contorted, so infinitely forlorn, Quast felt a tightening of the throat. Some of the faces were familiar despite the surprise, terror, or everlasting peace that had turned them into frozen masks. One belonged to Lieutenant Schreiner, who had commanded No 1

Company. Only a few days before, Quast and he had chatted about the Visigoths and wondered how many of their descendants were in the trenches opposite, ready to do battle with the same fearful relish as their forebears at the battle of the Catalaunian Fields. Wounded men trudged silently past. One of them was hailed by a sergeant who had just emerged from the dugout.

'Hey, Georg, why didn't you keep your head down?'

'Got too mad at the Ivans, that's why.'

The sergeant turned to Quast and Müller with a look of rueful admiration. 'Took off like bulls at a gate, they did, firing from the hip. A couple of boys from Schmidbauer's squad fired from the shoulder, unsupported. They stood up straight, like they were on a rifle range, and kept the Ivans' MGs quiet. Talk about guts!'

Karl and Gerhard turned up – radio operators attached to No 1 Company. 'Our set's a write-off,' said Karl. 'Grenade,' explained Gerhard. Everyone was looking grim and discontented. The forward companies had fought magnificently, Haldinger said, but lack of ammunition and slipshod battery-charging had cost them dearly. No 1 Company was down to half its original strength. 'Assault Battalion?' sneered someone. 'This outfit's just the same as any other; I knew it from the start.'

It was 3 A.M. when Quast installed his set in the czars' private railroad station. The command bunker, which had been driven through the foundations of the outer wall, ran beneath one of the platforms. He sneaked to the surface, curious to inspect a facility once reserved for the exclusive use of royal visitors to the palace lying somewhere in the grounds that were now a sea of churned-up mud. But all he saw was a railroad station in miniature: a small covered hall, two tracks, two platforms. Bullets had gnawed the edges of the window embrasures. Seen by the light of parachute flares, the unpretentious building looked strangely like a stage set. A rail spiralled up beside a shell hole. Rubble and debris littered platforms that had been

144

trodden by majesties, excellencies, and princesses in dainty patent leather boots. A star was winking through the rusty spider's web of the roof. The din of battle echoed from shattered walls adorned with the remains of plaster festoons; and there, where the carriages of the czars of all the Russias had wheeled so elegantly and headed for the nearby palace with its carved and gilded state apartments, a bunch of German riflemen were trudging through the mud, bowed with fatigue and insensible of bygone splendours. As he made his way back into the stinking, overheated cavern below ground, Quast promised himself a closer look when daylight came, but his resolution remained unfulfilled.

Scarcely had the Battalion moved into position, and scarcely had its heavy machine guns, mortars, and assault guns identified their targets and fields of fire, when the entire unit was withdrawn. Taking only their combat packs with them, the men were fed through a delousing station installed in an erstwhile factory. Every stitch of clothing they wore had to be fumigated, so they soon found themselves standing naked under showers mounted on the ceiling of a big oblong room with a tiled floor and walls of mustard-yellow brick. Tense and sullen faces relaxed, limbs stiff with cold thawed out.

Quast thought how pitiable they all looked without their uniforms. The weather-beaten red of their faces and necks made their white, often pimply bodies look obscene. There wasn't an ounce of surplus flesh on any of them. Many had protruding ribs. Many, too, had developed a lot of muscle, particularly in the arms and legs, as a result of endless marching laden with machine guns, mortar components, and ammunition boxes. In almost every case, scars told the story of their owners' campaign: a bullet wound acquired at the Dnieper, a graze at Feodosya, a gash at Gaitolovo, a sprinkling of brownish, ill-knit punctures inflicted by a mine near Vinyagolovo . . . Because they were all there as men, not privates or noncoms, and because they were universally conscious of their naked bodies, ribald remarks flew thick and fast. 'Hey,' Paul shouted to Albert, 'now I know why that fat nurse slapped your face when our train pulled out!' He pointed to Albert's shrivelled penis and guffawed. Albert filled his mouth with water and fired a jet at Paul's face. The shower room rang with laughter, but hilarity soon subsided. They were tired, and the water was growing cold.

A few hours later, the signallers were seated around a Christmas tree with the remnants of No 1 Company. Quast abhorred festive occasions that opened with stirring speeches, ran the gamut from joviality to sentimentality, and finally foundered in a sea of alcohol. To him they seemed a mockery – after all, what was there to celebrate? Though not addicted to guard duty, he was glad to find himself manning a well-concealed machine gun on the edge of the village. He peered over it at a dark fringe of forest and listened to the snow squeak under his boots. It was cold – twenty degrees below freezing.

Quite suddenly, a Russian night flier came whistling over the village with his engine switched off. His aim was poor. With their container tumbling after them, a cluster of small fragmentation bombs peppered the outskirts of the forest. Quast chuckled to himself and said, when the firecracker reports had died away, 'Merry Christmas, Ivan.' The men in the cottages behind him resumed their maudlin singing. He listened, aware that their gaiety was self-deceptive. Only a few days before, they'd been filled with homicidal fury, spattered with the blood of friends and comrades, standing up and blazing away from the shoulder. Now they were stewing in their stuffy, musty billets, drunkenly bawling 'Stille Nacht'.

He felt baffled and incensed, but not – he knew – by that. It was the shock of hearing that Heberle and Sand were dead – cut down in no-man's-land by the same machine-gun burst that had smashed Hapf's kneecaps.

146

Hapf was in a hospital ward, but his friend Herberle was dead. He could still see the sergeant's broad smile and the humorous, pugnacious, dependable look in his clear grey eyes, still see Sand's grin and the butt eternally glued to the corner of his mouth – and he, Quast, was standing here in this alien land, impotently staring at a line of trees beneath a star-studded, midnight-blue pincushion of a sky. He felt profoundly sad but very much alive. He'd stood there chuckling maliciously at a Russian pilot's lack of success. And all the time, Heberle was dead.

Early in the new year, they spent several weeks in Estonia, acting as a demonstration battalion for officers undergoing combat training. Their schedule, a regular one, included very little drill but plenty of field exercises.

One day, Quast was lying in the scrub beside Lieutenant Penkert, an austere, earnest-looking young man with horn-rimmed glasses and long, musicianly fingers. Earth was spurting from the open ground to their front. The mortars, which were using live ammunition, lifted their barrage to the small wood farther away. Penkert glanced at his watch and gave the order to advance. They worked their way across the open ground, textbook fashion. By the time they reached the wood, the mortars were pasting the slope beyond it. The trees were full of dummy figures. Lying, kneeling, firing from the hip, the riflemen gunned them down like targets in a fairground booth. Now for the reverse slope. They dashed out of the wood, but the barrage failed to lift. A hundred men lay pinned down by their own mortar fire. Panic-stricken, Penkert shouted to Quast, 'Tell them to up the range! They're firing short!' Quast was already yelling into the microphone, but there was no acknowledgement. It occurred to him that the trees might be hampering reception, so he jumped up and ran to a nearby mound. 'You're firing too short,' he yelled again, ' – too short, you bastards!' At last the barrage lifted to the trenches they were supposed to capture.

Quast watched, fascinated, as the riflemen advanced behind a curtain of fire, lobbing grenades, leaping on to dugout roofs, raking trenches with their automatic rifles, blinding a tank with smoke candles, and placing limpet bombs.

Then came a break. Quast, who was summoned in front of the officer trainees, stood there with his uniform torn and his army-issue glasses askew. The chief instructor gave him an extra evening pass for keeping his nerve. When one of the trianees asked him, jocularly, if he often exposed himself to friendly fire, he replied, 'Only when I have to, Lieutenant.'

The company regrouped for the next phase of the attack. The mortars concentrated on the slope ahead of them, which gently descended to another line of trees. Moving fast, they left the trenches and headed for their final objective. Lieutenant Penkert scurried back and forth between the first and second waves. Quast, with headset and microphone, followed at his heels. They were out of breath but in high spirits. The attack was on schedule and radio reception good. The exercise would be over in half an hour.

The first wave had already entered the wood when Quast's heart missed a beat. Half a dozen mortar bombs exploded among the trees, shrouding everything in smoke and dust. Quast transmitted the order to cease fire, but it was too late. Five men were down in the dirt, writhing and bleeding. Another lay still with his belly ripped open and his left leg severed at the knee. He was dead by the time they rolled him over. His chest was adorned with the Iron Cross ribbon, and Eastern Front medal, an assault badge, and a wound badge in silver, and he wore a Crimea badge on his sleeve. Somebody said, 'I've known him since Banja Luka.'

The exercise was discontinued.

That evening, Quast paid a visit to the local soldiers' café. He asked a dumpy Estonian girl to go to the movies with him, but she played hard to get. Eventually, she sauntered off with a sergeant who had a nice fat food parcel under his arm. Quast forgot about the girl and went to the movies alone, but he hardly noticed what was happening on the screen. The shock of the afternoon's events still lingered.

Next day he was detailed for potato-peeling. When the job was done, Müller told him to stay behind and clean up. Quast couldn't fathom the sergeant's smile as he left him to swab the floor and empty the brimming tubs. The fatigue party tramped off out of earshot. Quast found himself alone with Lena, a full-bosomed Estonian auxiliary of about twenty, with long legs, firm calves, a wide mouth, strong white teeth, and smiling blue eyes. The cookhouse was hot and humid, and condensation trickled down its green walls. Quast busied himself with broom and swab, but he couldn't take his eyes off Lena. The overall clung to her body, heavy with cookhouse steam, and he could see she had nothing else on. They'd exchanged a few words in recent weeks. The very sight of her made him want to touch her, lie against her, bury his fingers in her long, luxuriant fair hair. 'You could crack lice on Lena's tits,' the others used to say, but he didn't think of lice when he saw those breasts beneath her smock. It was quiet outside.

Lena said, 'I'll wipe the table. Will you do the floor?' She didn't move aside, so her rounded buttocks stared him in the face. Then she turned. He'd meant to say something flippant – call her 'Ice Maiden' or 'Flower of the North' and make her laugh, because he wanted to feast his eyes on the magnificent teeth and healthy pink gums that showed between her full lips – but when he looked up he saw she was smiling at him gravely. He swallowed hard. 'My little potato-peeler,' she said softly, 'why not take what you've been wanting all this time?'

And he did. Lena was a sensual, experienced girl. She let him think he was seducing her. Quast unbuttoned her

149

overall. He gazed at the thrusting, reddish-brown nipples, the alabaster skin with its delicate tracery of bluish veins, the round concavity of her navel, the mole above her copper-coloured fleece, the silken sheen of her thighs. His eyes took on the glazed look of a hungry baby finding ultimate contentment at its mother's breast. Lena praised his resourceful hands, delighted in his slender body, marvelled at the intensity of her young stallion's excitement. And so they sighed and moaned among the potato tubs, and the wooden bench creaked, and Lena babbled unintelligible things in lilting Estonian. Her climactic cry of rapture was drowned by a pair of fighter bombers that took off nearby and roared overhead.

14

AUTHOR: *Didn't you ever think of home, out there on the Leningrad front?*

QUAST: *Never. Pompous as it may sound, the battalion was my home.*

AUTHOR: *But one always hears of soldiers being homesick . . .*

QUAST: *Those with family ties, yes. Luckily, I didn't have any.*

AUTHOR: *What about your parents?*

QUAST: *I felt I was fighting for their sake as well as my own. The others had a duty to their wives and children. I was spared that responsibility.*

A few days later, Quast was detailed to set up a radio station in some trenches held by an engineer company. Although it had dawned on him, long before, that Lena had seduced him rather than the other way round, he felt no resentment. Gratitude surged through him as he plodded along the communication trench, gazing up at the night sky. Women like Lena were an anaesthetic against war, he reflected. At that moment, a high-velocity anti-tank shell whizzed overhead. He ducked and went his way. Within minutes, he'd installed himself in the command bunker. Headset on. Call sign. Viktor, Viktor, Viktor, do you read me? Receiving you strength five. 'QTR – do you have the exact time? KA – I have a message for you. KR – urgent.' Signaller Quast was at work. Lena? No time for her, not now.

He'd been lent to a company manning a position

northeast of the Sinyavino Heights. Although the scarred ground was mercifully blanketed in snow, he could guess at the storms of shot and shell that had swept it early in 1943, when the Russians carved out an overland route to the tormented, starving city of Leningrad.

He'd set off at dusk, hauling an *akya* laden with his rifle, pack, and radio set. He passed wrecked tanks and self-propelled guns, threaded his way between rocket batteries. The horizon stretched ahead of him in a flickering arc. Every now and then came the whipcrack of a rifle shot or a rattle of machine-gun fire. It was freezing hard, and the sled made a slithering sound in the snow. Having studied the map, he knew he'd have to leave the shell-torn remains of the forest and cross a hundred yards of open ground before reaching the shelter of the engineers' trenches. That he was prepared for, but not for the thrill of alarm that ran through him when an unseen sentry hailed him from the snow-swathed undergrowth.

'Another two minutes in that direction, and you'd better start talking Russian.'

'Christ, you startled me!'

'Better startled than dead, friend.'

'Where do I go?'

'Turn right past that KW1.' The sentry indicated a burned-out Russian tank. 'Follow the direction of the barrel, but be quiet about it.'

Quast found the trench. The engineer lieutenant was delighted to see him. 'Without a radio we might as well pack up and move out,' he said. 'You can see how we're placed.' Ah, thought Quast, so that was why they'd lent him an operator from the Assault Battalion. The position could only be reached over open ground. If things heated up and the telephone cables were cut, they'd be completely isolated.

Quast crawled through an entrance cut waist-high into the side of the trench. The cavern beyond this light shaft was far too low to enable a man to stand upright, and the air was thick enough to cut with a knife. A pencil-chewing sergeant was laboriously drafting a message. The lieutenant, a studiously nonchalant type, chatted to Quast about Teddy Stauffer and Benny Goodman, as though they were sitting in a sidewalk café on the Kurfürstendamm. Outside, the gunfire grew louder. A private crawled into the dugout. 'Corporal Melzer's wounded, Lieutenant – lost a little finger. He's on his way to the rear.' The lieutenant, who was whistling, casually nodded without interrupting his performance. Then he lit a cigarette. 'We always have trouble with the Ivans around this time,' he told Quast. 'They're pretty useful at grenade-throwing. Keep your eyes peeled if you go outside.' He donned his steel helmet, tapped the rim with his Walther, stuffed the gun into his pocket, and wriggled out of the bunker.

Sniper duels and grenade skirmishes apart, the next day brought nothing new. Quast peered over the parapet into no-man's-land. It was a bleak sight. Stretches of barbed wire, mounds of snow, drift-filled shell holes, burned-out tanks – such were the only features of this lethal, seemingly endless expanse. An icy wind drove powder snow into his face and drew a white veil over the northern skyline, beyond which lay the shores of Lake Ladoga. That night he was recalled to the Battalion.

A few days later, the Russians launched their major offensive against the weakened German lines in Ingermanland. The Battalion was shuttled to and fro, initially by train, behind the hard-pressed German defences. They were bombed and strafed while detraining at Krasnoye Selo. Although the attack left them grimy, perspiring, and edgy, it inflicted no casualties. Then the battered, mud-bespattered one-and-a-half-tonners took over again. The drivers grinned a weary welcome and transported them to a ridge with a pall of smoke hanging over it. There they waited in open order. Scout cars were coming over the brow of the hill, piled high with wounded. A motorcycle clattered past with two huddled figures in the sidecar. The man on the pillion seat was trailing a pennant of blood-stained bandage. From time to time, salvos of heavy Stalin-organ rockets slammed into the ridge. Splinters sped overhead with a frightful, sibilant whine. The waiting prove a strain on stomachs and bowels. Quast saw riflemen squatting everywhere with their pants down, some of them gripped by a kind of stage fright, others by mortal terror. Instead of being ordered to advance, however, they were sent crabwise along the front line, close enough to enjoy an alternation of heavy artillery fire and fragmentation bombs. According to the adjutant, the situation was so confused that Army didn't know where to commit the battalion first. The trucks picked them up again, only to deposit them beside the road an hour later.

They marched past country mansions that still preserved the aristocratic splendour of their czarist heyday. Fighters with red stars on their wings skimmed the rooftops, hammering away with cannons and machine guns. Quast took cover behind a *dacha* whose finely carved doorways and beams had been exposed to view by a direct hit. He couldn't tear himself away. One strip of faded wallpaper was hanging loose, and the plaster beneath had been faced with newsprint from the time when Leningrad boasted its own German-language daily.

'St Petersburg *Journal*, Thursday, January 1, 1876,' he read. 'The editorial offices of this newspaper are situated at No 4 Vozhnesyensky Prospekt, opposite the War Ministry and between the Malenkaya Morskaya and the Place of the Admiralty.' Reading on, he learned that displays of 'superior horsemanship, dressage, gymnastics, etc.' were presented daily at the Circus Ciniselli, and that 'dramatic and musical performances in the French, Russian, and German languages' could be enjoyed at the same hour – '7½ P.M.' – in the Berg Theatre. The Hotel Demuth reported that its 'latest arrivals from out of town' included 'Privy Councillor J. von Kube of Riga, Cornet Mauneskull of Warsaw, and Colonel Prince S. Golitsyn of

Moscow.' Pressure over Northeast Europe was high, with the temperature standing at minus twenty centigrade – a severe winter, in other words. The Warsaw Railroad Company announced the departure from St Petersburg of a train to Gatchina 'every afternoon at 5 (1st, 2nd, and 3rd Cl.).' It would, one presumed, be punctual, though 'today's Moscow mail train arrived here one hour and eleven minutes late.' A law report stated: 'Professor Butlerov has preferred criminal charges against his son, who is of age, on the grounds that he has violated Article 1566 of the Penal Code by marrying without paternal consent.' Pigheaded old fool, thought Quast.

An LaGG3 fighter came roaring over the rooftops. Küssel, a heavily built man with a rolling gait and a perpetual head cold that accounted for the grey woollen scarf he always wore, had to call Quast twice before he could bring himself to return from the days when people have lived and loved beside the Neva, not shot each other on sight.

Turmoil reigned throughout the frontline area. Roads and tracks were choked with columns of infantry, ammunition convoys, batteries of artillery, ambulances. Russian fighters and fighter-bombers harassed them at will. The Luftwaffe was nowhere to be seen.

Quast and Küssel were sent for by the CO. 'As of now,' he told them, 'you're our radio link with Gilbach's combat group on the Babelhof Heights – Battalion's just been attached to it. Looks as if we'll be covering the withdrawal in this sector. The whole damned outfit'll be in trouble unless you do your job, so good luck.'

Outside, in the lee of a barn, Orderly-Room Sergeant Werner drew Quast aside. 'Personal order from the Führer,' he whispered. 'Fight tooth and nail, hold your ground at all costs. The Babelhof Heights are vital, the C in C says. This is the clincher, from the sound of it. If the Ivans break through to Gatchina, they'll louse up our withdrawal. Gatchina's the key to the whole operation, or so the C in C keeps hollering. The longer we keep the Ivans out of there, the easier it'll be to pull our men back from the Sinyavino Heights and the marshes in the northeast. Think of it, Quast: all those guns, all those workshops and supply depots – not to mention the infantry. Man, will they have to wear out some shoe leather!'

A truck bound for the front had room for their radio but only one man. Küssel hauled himself aboard, sniffing as usual. While the truck was getting under way, they agreed to rendezvous at Tavalakhty, where the combat group's command post was said to be. They exchanged waves. The truck disappeared into the dusk, and Quast set off on foot.

The full extent of the northern skyline presented a familiar picture: flickering muzzle flashes, soaring flares, dancing flames, clouds of smoke daubed with red. Nearby guns made the night air tremble. The road was fringed and pockmarked with craters. Beside it lay a dead horse. The wreck of a burned-out truck twanged and creaked as the metal contracted. Overhead, flanked by the jet-black branches of the trees bordering the road, stars shone down from an inky-blue sky veiled in gossamer wisps of cloud.

Diminutive though he felt against such a vast and dramatic backdrop, Quast's heart beat faster. But it was the Battalion's fate, not his own, that preoccupied him. Only now, as he trudged all alone, past a row of freshly dug graves, towards the flaming horizon, did he sense how strong his ties with this group of men had become. He saw the major, lithe and restless as a racehorse. He saw Heinz Müller, with his slow smile and deliberate movements. He saw Schröder, whose yellow fingers were unimaginable without a cigarette between them, and Lieutenant Heide, the combat-patrol specialist, affectionately patting his Russian submachine gun. Quast knew that the battalion was reserved for the toughest spots of all, but now that it was going into action *en bloc*, he and Küssel had been parted from their comrades and attached to the remnants of a combat group that would naturally look after its own men first and a battalion of outsiders second.

It seemed an age before the Babelhof Heights loomed out of the darkness on his right. Just where the road cut into the rising ground, a sentry stopped him. 'That's far enough,' he was told. 'The Ivans are dug in up ahead.' He turned off right, and there was Küssel standing beside the partly unloaded truck. They drove up a steep gorge to a group of buildings interspersed with tall, bizarrely shaped trees. Above the road, which wound down into the plain behind them, stood a gloomy house with a paved forecourt. The upper windows stared blankly into the night like hollow eye sockets, but activity reigned in the vaulted cellars, which ran deep into the hillside. They had reached headquarters.

15

AUTHOR: *But defeat was inevitable. Surely you must have known that by then?*

QUAST: *We had more immediate worries, like maintaining radio contact and saving men and equipment. Agonizing over the broader issues we left to other people.*

They reported to a captain who hoarsely instructed them to set up their radio link at once, underlining his words with nervous gestures. They had to hug the wall of the underground passage to make room for men toting boxes outside. The command post was being dismantled. Quast and Küssel installed their set in a cramped, thick-walled chamber as close as possible to the exit. Signallers from other units were at work in the adjacent cellars. There was no time to sound them out on the general situation. Corporal Wellmann, of their own signal platoon, came through loud and clear. The Assault Battalion's counter-attack had been checked by heavy fire from German twenty-ones. Lieutenant Heide's company had reached the ridge, which had been given up for lost, but was withdrawing because of losses inflicted by friendly fire. The other companies were engaged in house-to-house fighting. The Battalion, which was picking up stragglers and survivors from other formations, had lost contact with the units on either flank.

Quast removed his headset and joined Küssel in the entrance. They listened to the noises outside. Some mortars opened up on the right, their salvos punctuated by flurries of rifle and submachine-gun fire. The head-quarters staff had now moved out, all except for a pallid young lieutenant and two signallers ensconced in a fusty-smelling cellar. Quast and Küssel were told to stay on listening watch and await further orders. The firing grew steadily louder, making it hard to hear. They decided to move the set outside, into one of the slit trenches near the building, because they needed all the reception they could get.

Wellmann came through again, abruptly followed by the CO's incisive voice: 'We're holding our ground. Enemy penetration on both flanks, depth unknown. What's happening at your end?'

Quast deliberated. Should he tell Haldinger that the building was already under small-arms fire? That the forecourt was thick with the dead? That two Russian tanks had just rattled past and were racing down the road towards the plain? He confined himself to saying: 'HQ withdrawing south. Two enemy tanks heading for the plain. Southern edge of Tavalakhty still in German hands.'

The firing eased. The Russians seemed to be regrouping for a further attack at daybreak. Half an hour later, Battalion urgently – 'repeat, urgently' – requested infor-mation about enemy movements on either flank and in its rear. All the wounded had been loaded into vehicles, but Haldinger was disinclined to send them back, because fighting appeared to be in progress behind him. Quast and Küssel exchanged worried glances. Quast chewed his lip, Küssel pulled nervously at his cigarette and sniffed. Diving back into the shelter of the cellars, they found them deserted. There was nobody left to answer Batta-lion's inquiries. One of the signallers was still at his post. He didn't know where the pale lieutenant and the other signaller had gone, and combat group headquarters wasn't answering. His hands trembled as he spoke. 'The Ivans'll be here any minute,' he said. 'What about us?'

Quast looked outside. Isolated shots could be heard. Dawn had broken, but a mist was rising. He said, 'If there aren't any infantry left in front of us, we'll pack up.'

An indistinct figure crept cautiously up the slope towards them, keeeping low. They cocked their rifles and took cover. The figure paused among the bodies in the forecourt, slunk on, paused again, and peered around. Then they identified the steel helmet. It was a German infantryman. He whistled with relief when he saw who they were.

'I was just going to turn back – I thought you'd all cleared out. They sent me to collect two radio teams. Are you them?'

Quast signalled 'Changing position' and switched off. Very quietly, because they suddenly detected Russian voices on the far side of the building, they carried the sets down the slope and put them on a horse-drawn sled.

They worked their way back through deep snow. The road, which they shunned for safety's sake, was on their right – they could sometimes sense rather than see it through swaths of mist that reduced it to a blurred grey ribbon. They also heard the roar of engines. Massive grey shapes – Russian tanks – loomed up for an instant, then vanished. They lost their way and couldn't find it by ear, because the cotton-wool vapour swallowed almost every sound. At last the road reappeared ahead of them.

By the time the mist cleared, flooding the plain with morning sunlight, they'd reached Aleksandrovskoye. The tiny church had a squat, sturdy tower, and snow-laden trees flanked the churned-up road. Bunkers had been dug beside it. They installed themselves in the open, among some stacks of timber. The frequency was repeatedly jammed by powerful German and Russian transmitters, so they switched to Morse. Battalion called first: 'QRM [Enemy jamming].' Then 'KR – urgently request order to withdraw. Position becoming untenable. Enemy attacks repulsed with heavy losses. Reconnaissance has so far failed to detect any enemy in the direction of Taitsy.' They decided to bypass the usual channels and request a ruling from the combat group commander himself.

Several officers were standing beside the road with drawn pistols. Toiling wearily towards them across the open ground to their front, some in groups and others in extended order, were scores of infantrymen. The officers waved their arms like windmills. 'Get back up front – at once, do you hear?' But the soldiers kept coming. The machine gunners' number twos raised their ammunition boxes and inverted them: empty. The riflemen opened their ammunition pouches: ditto. Their movements were leaden, their faces pale and numb with fatigue. From beyond the ridge on the skyline came the swelling, dying roar of Shturmoviks strafing the rear guard – deluging them with fragmentation bombs and bursts of gunfire.

Brushing past a sentry who ported his rifle and tried to bar their path, Quast and Küssel blundered down the steps of the command bunker. There was something eerie about the scene below ground. The square chamber, which was barely head height, received little illumination from the window slit below the roof. Against the wall, an officer's campaign chest; in the centre, supported by two trestles, an old door serving as a table; on the latter, maps and a carbide lamp. The grizzled colonel was propped on his elbows. His grey face was deeply lined, his eyes glittered feverishly in their dark sockets, and his jaw and the environs of his mouth were frosted with stubble. Beside him, frowning at the sudden intrusion, stood a horse-faced captain. In front of these spectral figures, whose crumpled uniforms were open at the neck, could be seen a bottle, two glasses, and a plateful of cigarette butts. The air was thick with smoke.

Quast approached the table and saluted. 'Signallers Quast and Küssel, Colonel, on detachment from the Assault Battalion. I urgently request the Colonel's permission to address him direct.'

'Go ahead.'

'Major Haldinger requests an order to withdraw.'

'Ah yes, the Assault Battalion.' The colonel exchanged a weary glance with his adjutant. 'As soon as I've any orders for them, Signaller, you'll be informed.'

Quast stood fast. 'They're as good as cut off, Colonel. All the wounded are still up front.'

'Their flanks are completely exposed,' Küssel chimed in. 'It's now or never.'

The colonel stared at them both with unseeing eyes. Quast, who sensed that the man's nerves were at breaking point, was afraid he'd kick them out. Instead, he said quietly, 'Signal them as follows: Withdraw at own discretion.'

They raced back up the steps. Quast got through in seconds. 'Withdraw,' he yelled. 'Withdraw at own discretion – be quick, for heaven's sake!' Wellmann replied, 'Message received and understood.' Then, after a brief pause, 'Moving now. Out.' The relief in his voice was almost tangible.

Ten minutes later they tossed their G Pack into a passing scout car and climbed on the running boards. A trio of IL2s streaked overhead at zero feet. Their bombs landed beside the road. Burst of gunfire ripped shingles off the roof of the church and peppered its walls, but Quast and Küssel were unhurt.

Dusk was falling when the first members of the Assault Battalion straggled into the farmyard, and it was dark by the time Lieutenant Schwarz, a short, thickset company commander, called the roll. Quast looked on, appalled, with Heinz Müller standing beside him. Helplessly, he gripped the sergeant's arm. Only yesterday, when the Battalion moved up, its strength had been in the region of five hundred men. Now, barely two hundred and fifty were arrayed on the flagstones in front of the stables. What had happened to the hundred stretcher cases?

The survivors were dismissed to the stables, where they

162

sprawled in the straw and awaited fresh orders. Quast picked his way among the rows of silent men. 'What about the wounded?' he asked. 'Where's the CO?' They shrugged and avoided his eye. Sergeant Leschinski, of the runners' squad, was leaning against the wall of a wagon shed, deathly pale and chewing a straw. 'Leschi, you were with the CO. Where is he?' Leschi said, 'Haldinger's dead.' Then he unburdened himself.

After assigning a rear guard and fixing the companies' order of march, the CO had driven to the southern outskirts of the village to supervise the departure of the trucks carrying the wounded – likewise of the company that was to withdraw along the road while others covered the flanks. Leschi, seated in the back of Haldinger's scout car, was to fire a green flare as soon as they reached the exit. This would be the signal for the rear guard to begin its withdrawal, holding the enemy off until the convoy was far enough along the road and the last of the riflemen were clear of the village and deployed in open ground beyond. Lieutenant Schridde was sitting beside Leschi, and a man with a bullet through the lung had been lashed to the canvas roof.

The scout car approached the final bend in the village street. The driver swore at the potholes. Haldinger produced a map from his pouch and said, 'Go slow. As soon as we round the bend, I'll hop out. You pull over and keep the engine running – and you, Leschinski, await my order.' Leschi ran a last-minute check on his flare pistol and looked up. Just then, Russian submachine gunners in white camouflage jackets broke cover on both sides of the road. Their opening bursts shattered the windshield. The driver and the CO slumped forward. Schridde gave a yelp of pain. He and Leschi dived sideways out of the scout car. The wounded man on the roof was shouting desperately and coughing blood. Leschi raised the flare pistol and was about to pull the trigger when a Russian approached the vehicle with his submachine gun at the ready.

163

Leschi swallowed hard. 'I thought, shall I carry on and tip off the rear guard – you know, Döhlker and No 2 Company – or shall I give it to the Ivan? I only had a split second to make up my mind, but boy, you've no idea how long it seemed. So I . . .' He drew a deep breath. 'So I put my own hide first. Yes, sir, that's what I did, God help me!' His Adam's apple bobbed again. 'I shot the Ivan in the chest and ran – anything to get away from that road and the Ivans . . .'

But his nightmare wasn't over yet. Cowering behind a bush, Leschi watched trucks laden with wounded charge wildly through the Russian roadblock. The drivers veered off to avoid two craters, travelling much too fast. The riflemen detailed to escort them couldn't follow in the deep snow. In any case, they were under attack from the flanks and rear by Russians who had lain in ambush on the edge of the village and were now swarming across the open ground beyond. Camouflaged by their white coveralls, yet another group of lurking Russians pumped tracer into the convoy from a position out in the fields. Almost instantly, the gas tanks and reserve cans exploded. The trucks became fireballs wreathed in oily black smoke, and from their midst came the dying screams of the wounded. The riflemen were powerless to help. Encircled and pinned down in the snow, they fought for survival at point-blank range. And Leschi, unnoticed behind his bush, witnessed the tragedy from a distance of two hundred yards.

'But then, thank God, Döhlker and his boys turned up. He'd obviously heard the firing and guessed what had happened. The Ivans must have thought they could wipe us out, but Döhlker taught them different. He tackled them like he was out on an exercise – textbook stuff. I didn't know whether to laugh or cry.' Leschi made an inarticulate noise in his throat. 'If you want the truth, I wept like a baby. It was the sight of those trucks that did it. Schmiedel, Schmidtsberger, Kutte, Gustav, Willi – all gone, all burned to a crisp.' The last word ended on a sob.

Quast stared at him transfixed, at a loss for words. 'But Leschi, there wasn't a thing you could do.'

Leschi shook his head. 'Sure there was,' he said. 'I knew I should have given the signal, but I couldn't. I should have fired in the air, but I didn't. It was my fault the rear guard got there too late. I'm yellow, that's what. They're all down on me, every last one of them. Jesus, how can I go on living – how can I ever go home with that on my conscience? There isn't a God in heaven can help me now . . .'

Leschi's nerves had given way. He stood there shaking, with tears coursing down his haggard cheeks. None of the men nearby could muster any words of consolation. Even if the right words had existed, they were too far gone to have thought of them.

Quast looked around uncomprehendingly. This bunch of torpid, dull-eyed men – could they really be his Battalion?

Then Schwarz's voice came echoing across the yard. 'Prepare to move out!' They were going into action again.

16

AUTHOR: *For a teenager, you underwent some pretty frightful experiences. What on earth kept you going – loyalty to the Führer?*

QUAST: *The Führer? We didn't spare him a thought at that stage – after all, he never toured the Russian front. Loyalty did come into it, though. I know it's a suspect word these days – people think it's out of date – but it did play a big part then, even if none of us said so out loud. Letting my comrades down when they were just as dependent on me as I was on them – that would have been unthinkable.*

The village was deserted. The doors were unlocked and the rooms denuded of their meagre furnishings, though a bench or chest could sometimes be seen in a corner, or a bucket of ashes beside a cold hearth, or a tub of *soloniye ogurtsi* – pickles – abandoned on a shelf. Wisps of dirty yellow straw scudded across the snow-covered cottage gardens.

The men of the rearguard company had dug in among some empty barns on the outskirts. The company command post was centrally sited in a log cabin half embedded in the ground. The pond beside it was frozen over, its icy surface swept clear of snow by the wind.

Quast leaned against the wall, resentfully watching a radio operator from another unit struggling with his Morse key. He himself had no radio. Sergeant Schröder, of the signal platoon, had thrust a canvas pouch full of cipher and frequency schedules into his hand and told him not to let them out of his sight because they were top secret. Then he'd sent him forward to the village, promising to meet him there with a G Pack and a second signaller.

But neither the sergeant nor the second signaller had turned up, only this two-man team from God knew what outfit – a pair of bungling amateurs. The Russians had turned up too, far sooner than expected. The outskirts of the village were already under mortar fire, and an attack in company strength – more of an armed reconnaissance – had been driven off. Now the firing had increased, and he, Quast, was obliged to stand there idly with a pouch in his hand and watch. The door opened.

'Schröder!' he said by way of greeting. 'Where's that set?'

'Eh?' The sergeant frowned. 'It came up with the ammunition truck.'

'The hell it did.'

'Damnation!' Schröder flung a half-smoked cigarette on the floor and mashed it with his heel. 'Two signallers, no set, and trouble brewing.'

The rearguard company commander, a wiry young lieutenant, lost patience with the man at the Morse key. 'Can't you speed it up?' he snapped. 'We need that artillery support at once, man.'

'I know, Lieutenant; I'm – '

The rest of the signaller's stammered apology was drowned by a salvo of Russian mortar bombs. The lieutenant darted outside. Five minutes later he returned, out of breath.

'Well? I need that assault battery, otherwise the Russians will make mincemeat of us. Try again, Signaller. Send this: Urgently request – '

Quast broke in. 'Just a minute, Lieutenant. There's a better way.'

'What do you mean?'

'Of getting in touch with them. I know where they are – let me handle it.'

167

'All right, but be quick.'

Three minutes later, Quast and his pouch were speed-ing to the rear through a hail of mortar fire. It made him nervous, having to look after the papers. He'd tried to unload them on Schröder, but the sergeant had merely tapped his forehead in ironical silence. He sprinted along a hedge, trying to relax and breathe steadily. Then a rifle cracked on his right, sending a shower of twigs and withered leaves on to the frozen farm track. So the Russians had already outflanked the village. If they nabbed him, was he expected to eat every item in the pouch, and if so, which one first? Regulations were all very well, but they weren't designed for emergencies.

The country house had yellow stuccoed walls. The signal centre was installed in an oriel on the ground floor. A sergeant was standing stiffly at attention beside the radio set, and the foursquare figure facing him belonged to Captain Bosch, of the assault battery. Captain Bosch was loudly telling the sergeant what he thought of his radio link. He looked like a bulldog – he even sounded like one – but his tone became ferociously amiable when he saw Quast.

'Ah, there you are. I've got four lovely ten-point-fives out there, all set to open fire. See if you can get through, and make it snappy!'

The radio operator was looking distraught. 'Get lost,' Quast told him, and settled himself at the key. He quickly raised Schröder, whose missing G Pack had turned up, and passed on the data compiled by the rearguard com-pany commander. Bosch growled his orders by field telephone to the ten-point-fives, which were lurking among some bales of straw in the grounds. Muzzles flashed fire at the northern sky, shell cases clanged on frozen stubble, mugs danced on top of the radio set, and slivers of shattered window-pane tinkled to the floor.

The guns were on target, thanks to the lieutenant's careful plotting. Quast could divine such minor corrections as were necessary even before Schröder passed them on. Before half an hour was up, the Lieutenant reported that the Russians were pulling back. The village was clear of enemy once more.

Valuable time had been gained. Time enough to tend the wounded and send them back, haul heavy guns to the rear, bring up ammunition and fuel, and evacuate supply depots – time enough, too, to recover the dead and bury them in shell holes. Quast stood up and handed the headset to Bosch's sergeant. Bosch patted him on the back and gave a contented grunt.

His mission completed, Quast rejoined the rear guard. He paused beside a truck with a broken axle. A stack of combat rations had spilled over the tailgate. Passing soldiers had ripped open the packs and swiped the cigarettes, but he pocketed some candy bars for safety's sake – you never could tell when more supplies would turn up. To left and right of him, engines were grinding away in the distance. They sounded like Russians, he thought, stuffing chocolate into his mouth. Who would make it to the next village first, friend or foe?

The men of the rear guard got there first. They established a defensive position, repelled some Russian reconnaissance patrols, peered into the darkness, and waited. Quast hunkered down in a foxhole with his G Pack. Lieutenant März, the battalion adjutant, jumped in beside him. He took off his helmet, mopped his brow, replaced the helmet on the back of his head, and inserted a fresh magazine into his submachine gun. 'All right, Quast,' he said, 'let's have some music.'

They crouched there shoulder to shoulder on a sheaf of damp straw, each with an earphone clamped to his ear. Quast returned to the frequency that had so often entertained them in the past. Machine guns hammered, rifle grenades exploded, mortar bombs plopped into the snow, and Russian gunners zeroed in on the village, but there they crouched, engrossed in the delights of BBC

London. 'Hold zat tiger,' they hummed, tapping their feet in time to the tune, 'Hold zat tiger.' Then someone nearby called März's name. He handed the earphone back, sang out, 'Hold zat tiger!' and vanished into the gloom.

Two dozen infantrymen on the edge of the village were simulating the firepower of a full-strength company. Machine gunners changed position at random intervals, riflemen darted to and fro betweeen cottages and barns, firing a shot here and a shot there. Quast was sitting on the floor of an icy room with his torn and crumpled cipher sheets shovelled together beneath a crude kitchen table. It was 3 A.M., misty, dark, and well below freezing. He set fire to the papers. Though out of date, they might still prove informative if they fell into enemy hands. A voice from the doorway urged him to hurry. He ground the ashes to dust, picked up his rifle and radio set, and crunched his way along a debris-strewn passage to the front door. The threshold and surrounds were wet with blood. Lieutenant Heide had been standing there twenty minutes earlier, when a mortar-bomb splinter lopped off the top of his skull. He was still conscious when they carried him off on a stretcher, but would he survive such a terrible wound? Would he ever recover, that quiet, inoffensive, inconspicuous young man with the ready smile and the ability to become so different a person – so fearsome a hunter of his own species – when the chips were down?

Dawn was breaking. Stealthily, they padded across the field in single file. Quast, who couldn't resist a backward look at the village he'd never seen by daylight, brought up the rear. Franz, the man just ahead of him, suddenly slowed down. 'Mum's the word!' he whispered, peering furtively from side to side. Dim figures could be seen digging foxholes: Russians! Nothing about their movements betrayed any hostile interest in the other dim figures trudging through their lines, whom they obviously mistook for friends. Just then, Quast noticed that someone had tagged on behind him: fur cap, sheepskin jacket, map case, soft brown boots. Deliberately closing up on Franz, he whispered, 'There's an Ivan behind us!' Then he stepped aside and pretended to fumble in his pocket. The Russian ambled past him with his head down, yawning. Franz swung round, rifle at the ready. The Russian half turned to run, but Quast was too quick for him. He yanked the heavy Tokarev from its holster and held the barrel to his lips like an admonitory forefinger. '*Derzhi yazik!*' he said with a meaningful look. 'Quiet!' With the Russian between them, they silently joined the others.

Once clear of the danger zone, they all crowded round the prisoner, relieved him of his map case, scrutinized and fingered his sheepskin jacket. 'My, isn't that pretty!' Sergeant Schröder said admiringly. 'I didn't know they still existed.' The Russian, a well-groomed captain of twenty-five or so, was almost weeping with rage at the unheroic blunder that had sentenced him to captivity. The men soon lost interest in him. To them, he was merely one more embodiment of the fresh, well-rested, formidable enemy who was driving them from his country with the same remorseless vigour as they, the Germans, had shown when overrunning it two and a half years earlier. The sight of him brought it home to them how down-at-heel, exhausted, and ill-equipped they now were. Seated between two lightly wounded escorts in a cart laden with blood-stained bodies, he ignored his captors and stared into space with a look of hatred and contempt. They were glad when the cart disappeared behind some ruined buildings.

Mean little houses flanked the village street in two squat rows. In the open ground on either side, remnants of the battalion had taken cover behind bushes, barns, and mounds of earth. They had evolved a defensive system in which radio communication played the part of nerve fibres linking groups commanded by one or more officers and noncoms drawn from the depleted rifle companies. They

171

reminded Quast of unicellular organisms forever changing shape and cohering, sometimes in chains, sometimes in clusters. Such was the withdrawal of what had once been a compact, close-knit battalion, and the greatest threat to its progress was a breakdown in communication.

Quast and Gerhard were seated over their set in the kitchen of a house in the centre of the village. Quast transmitted an urgent request for ammunition, field dressings, and food supplies. Then he hailed Lieutenant Schwarz, who was hurrying past the window, and gave him the combat group commander's response: 'Make do with what you've got. Am sending light flak support.' The lieutenant shook his head and scowled.

By now, the Russians had targeted the centre of the village. The kitchen door blew in with a crash, blasted off its hinges by a mortar bomb. Gerhard crouched in a corner, coughing. Quast had fallen off his bench. Schwarz peered in through the shattered window. 'Better come out of there,' he shouted. 'The walls won't hold up much longer!' They dashed outside and looked along the street. A tracked vehicle with quadruple pom-poms mounted on it thundered past. The steel footplates that enlarged the gun platform were folded down; the tracks rattled and squeaked. The gunner waved to them.

Quast dived into a cellar and set up the radio again. No contact. 'It's the aerial,' said Gerhard. 'Hang on.' A stray length of field telephone cable was snaking across the cellar floor. Gerhard scribbled some calculations on a scrap of paper and muttered, 'For this frequency we'll need ten yards.' He cut off the requisite footage and towed it outside. Quast connected the other end to the set. Contact re-established.

Outside, bursts of machine-gun fire were whistling along the street. Lieutenant Schwarz shouted down the cellar stairs. 'Prepare to move out!' Quast said to Gerhard, 'If the Ivans see us in the street with that G Pack, they'll use us for target practice.'

Gerhard was the signal platoon's most slovenly member. Whenever there was an inspection, his lopsided cap, flapping ammunition pouches, and sagging belt assured him of a place in the rear rank. Now he gave Quast an impish grin and produced a mangled tube of toothpaste from his haversack. Squeezing the contents into his palm, he spread the white goo over the rear and sides of the G Pack like a child playing mud pies. Peppermint mingled with the acrid smell of explosive. 'Terrific,' he said; 'with that on my back, I won't have to worry about BO'

The mobile anti-aircraft unit came rattling slowly back past the house. The gunner and his two loaders were lying dead beside their pom-poms, killed by whatever had riddled the gun shield with holes. The driver had a bloodstained bandage round his head. The gun commander was kneeling up on the passenger seat, firing sub-machine-gun bursts to the rear. Quast and Gerhard stood in the cellar entrance and waited for the vehicle to go by. A rifleman blundered down the steps, almost knocking them over. 'Cover us,' Quast told him, and they surfaced fast.

More riflemen were standing, kneeling, or lying in the shelter of doorways and projecting walls on both sides of the street. 'Run like hell,' one of them shouted. 'We're pulling back any minute' They pounded up a slight incline with Gerhard and the radio in the lead.

A runner came sprinting to meet them. 'Turn left beyond the railroad track,' he gasped. 'Schwarz wants you.' Gerhard laughed. 'Never a dull moment,' he said. Then he fell flat on his face and his helmet skittered across the road. Quast shouted, 'Gerhard!' When he rolled him over, he saw that Gerhard didn't have a face any more: the bullet had gone through the back of his head. Moist-eyed, Quast knelt beside the dead man. He pocketed his papers and tugged the G Pack off his shoulders. 'Give me a hand, someone!' he called desperately. The street was being swept by gusts of automatic fire. He beckoned to

173

some riflemen for help, but the three men nearest him were kneeling with their backs to him. As they jumped up and ran past, one of them yelled, 'Beat it, you boy scout!'

Quast took Gerhard's lifeless body by the wrists and dragged it into the gutter. Brick dust spurted from a pattern of holes in the wall beside him. He let the limp arms fall. Without looking back, he plodded on in a kind of stupor, across the railroad track and into the outskirts of a wood. 'Where've you been?' barked Schwarz. 'Get a move on, man!'

17

AUTHOR: *While we're on the subject, was there any pent-up hatred or contempt for the Führer?*

QUAST: *Not really. Germany came first in all our thoughts. The Führer's image had faded.*

AUTHOR: *Faded to such an extent that you felt impelled to save a deserter from the firing squad – an ex-Red Army man?*

QUAST: *That had nothing to do with it. Our own prospects were bleak enough, but that poor devil was really between the devil and the deep blue sea.*

When darkness fell, the remnants of the Battalion mustered at a road junction outside Gatchina. A barn was blazing fiercely nearby, and the crackling flames shed a fitful light on the men's weary faces. Flares were soaring into the sky in a wide arc – an indication of how far the Russians had advanced. The overcast glowed crimson in some places, pink and white in others. The sound of small-arms fire was largely muffled by a dense belt of blue-black forest to their rear, but they could hear the swelling, fading rumble of heavy artillery.

Schwarz ordered them to fall in and called the roll. His voice became steadily more subdued.

'No 1 Company?'

'Two NCO's and fourteen men.'

'No 2?'

'One NCO and eleven men.'

'No 3?'

'One NCO, six men.'

'No 4? . . . No 5? . . ., Then: 'Engineer Platoon?'

'No one left, Lieutenant.'

Lieutenant 'Babyface' Habermann's eyes glistened in the firelight. Surreptitious tears? Grief, exhaustion, despair?

Lieutenant März was standing next to Quast. 'Not exactly what they taught us in school, eh?' All at once, Quast had a vision of the chemistry teacher they'd always been able to side-track when a test was in the offing. 'Sir, tell us about the time you went over the top at Ypres,' they'd chorus, desperate to avoid betraying their ignorance. And he, with the light of battle in his eyes, would mount the podium and proclaim, 'I drew my pistol and jumped on to the firing step. Then I turned and looked down at my gallant lads in field grey. "Men," I cried, " – men, we're going to knock hell out of 'em!"'

Schwarz said, 'Tomorrow we go through Gatchina. At our present rate of progress, we ought to reach the outskirts by early afternoon. We've got to get through there and back to rear echelon. If we let the Russians wipe us out, Army'll cross this Battalion off its books. We don't want that, do we? So keep out of trouble. Don't get shanghaied into any scratch formations, and steer clear of military police patrols.' He smiled, 'That's off the record, mind you.'

The Russians were on their heels next morning. The combat group's radio station had stopped transmitting. Quast was relieved. Orders that didn't reach them didn't have to be carried out. He suspected that Schwarz shared his sentiments.

They were approaching a gravel pit when a ration truck crawled past. 'Can't find my outfit,' the driver called. 'Got a whole load of stew on board. Anyone who's hungry, follow me!' Quast was hungry – being under twenty, he was officially entitled to extra rations but seldom got them. He ran after the truck, which pulled up in the quarry itself. Soon every mess kit was brimming. Presum-

176

ably the ration NCO and his driver couldn't wait to empty their containers and head for the rear again. Then they heard the rocket salvo – a screaming crescendo that sounded like the trump of doom. Ladle in hand, the ration NCO dived off the tailgate into the cluster of men holding mess kits. The salvo straddled them. Quast was scared but determined to save his stew. As soon as the dust cleared, he looked up. Two men were silent and motionless, two more writhing in agony. The ration NCO lay groaning on top of the corporal next to Quast, his blood diluting the gravy that dripped off the rim of the corporal's helmet.

Gatchina was ablaze. They'd entered the town by way of Czars' Gate. Now the light was fading. The buildings they skirted cast shadows whose obscurity was intensified by clouds of pitch-black smoke. Flames gushed from the roofs and upper floors of timber-framed houses. By their flickering light, Quast saw a field battery come racing down the street. When it slowed for a moment or two, he hitched a ride on a limber. Nobody gave him a second glance. The surviving members of the Battalion had been instructed to make their way through the town in small independent groups and rendezvous on the road to Ziverskaya. At nightfall, Quast and a handful of men – the remnants of No 2 Company – took cover in the hallway of an abandoned house. A corpse was lying on the passage floor amid crusts of dried mud and puddles of melted snow. In default of enough time to bury him, someone had folded the dead man's hands on his chest.

They reviewed the situation and reached a unanimous decision: now wasn't the time to get drafted into some makeshift unit full of strangers determined to survive at their comrades' expense. Peering out the door, they saw some trucks grind to a halt. The street was choked. Quast ran over to the nearest driver. 'Room for eight men?'

'I didn't hear. Got any cigarettes?' One of their number tossed a hundred cigarettes on to the passenger seat.

177

'There's MPs up ahead,' said the driver. 'Under that tarpaulin, quick!'

They crawled beneath the tarpaulin and secreted themselves among some empty fuel drums. The driver had been carrying two wounded men. He lashed the tarpaulin down and dumped them on top. The truck moved off. A minute later, with a squeal of brakes, it halted at the checkpoint. Lying there in the dark, Quast had a vivid mental picture of two MPs stalking suspiciously around the truck, hands on hips. He heard the crunch of their boots, then the driver's voice.

'I'm running out of time, Sergeant Major. If I'm not back soon with more gas and ammunition, my pals up front can kiss the girls good-bye.'

After an interminable pause, the truck moved off again. It dropped them at an intersection. They crawled out, blinking.

The driver said, 'You're taking a vacation, aren't you? Be honest.'

Schröder glowered at him. 'Führer command, we obey – remember the old slogan?'

'Sure, so what?'

'Well, it's been updated. Führer command, we take the rap – that's the latest version. These men here are all that's left of a rifle company. So beat it, you scrounging son of a bitch!'

The driver watched them go, shaking his head.

It was early March. Twelve months before, almost to the day, Quast had alighted on the platform at Gatchina, filled with zeal and burning with curiosity. It seemed years ago. The new, skinnier Quast wore a look of weary but wary composure. Coltish no longer, his movements were economical and purposeful. He'd learned to sleep in any position, any situation, be it only for five short minutes. He could munch bread, tap out a message, and gauge the progress of a battle with one ear trained on the pandemonium outside. He could be simultaneously torpid and alert. It had never occurred to him that he would study clods of frozen earth, blades of withered grass, chunks of masonry, and slivers of splintered wood as closely, intently, and single-mindedly as he did during those endless minutes when war's fiery breath fanned his cheek, when the gates of hell opened, when he hugged the ground in total indifference to all but the prospect of extinction.

They'd been on the retreat since mid January 1944. The Battalion never regained its full strength, even though many casualties rejoined it fresh from field hospitals or spells of convalescent leave at home. Every day brought another boisterous reunion with some such member of the 'old gang' back from the dead. Batches of replacements arrived too – pallid, edgy, inexperienced teenagers who were often sent into action as soon as they jumped off a truck. Many of them lay waxen-cheeked in the snow before they ever got to see a Russian.

Quast now knew something of what was going on in Russia, but his bewilderment persisted. He'd had to modify many of his scornful preconceptions about the enemy, likewise his comforting picture of an invincible Greater German Army.

'Our watchword now is "Don't give an inch!" We stand at the approaches to our homeland. Every backward step would bring the war closer to Germany by air and sea.'

Hearing this order of the day from the commander in chief of the Eighteenth Army, Quast acknowledged that it would be better to defend his country here, far from its borders, and thereby preserve it from the treatment it had meted out to Russia. But hadn't the original intention been to restore Germany's prestige and gain her people a new domain in the East? First these glittering objectives; now this dogged defence of a few peasant cottages, a patch of marsh or forest. First an unbroken string of easy victories; now this pain and mutilation, these overturned trucks and dynamited guns, these abandoned supply depots and blazing fuel dumps. It didn't add up.

German supremacy in Europe? They'd be lucky if their country survived at all, Quast told himself, and ended by clinging to this idea. *That* was why he had to do his duty: for the sake of national survival.

But there was little time to dwell on such thoughts. The Russians gave them no peace, and anyway, who wanted to think when the only product of reflection was bitterness and doubt?

Just as battalions, companies, and platoons were placed under outside command when a gap needed plugging, so signal detachments and individual signallers were sometimes lent to other units. Quast found himself on loan yet again. 'Can't be helped,' März told him as he stood there looking sulky, like a child whose parents are packing him off to an unloved aunt. 'Don't worry, we'll ask for you back the first chance we get. Chin up!'

He hitched a ride in a battered rattletrap of a supply truck and headed into the ebb tide of the German withdrawal. When he finally reported to the headquarters of his new combat group, numb and stiff after riding through the night for hours on end, he was told that the formation had been badly mauled and taken out of the line. In other words, he wasn't needed after all. So much the better, he thought. Squeezing on to the box of a one-horse cart piled high with supplies, he sat there as it threaded its way into the endless stream of retreating vehicles.

Alex, the driver, was a thirty-year-old Russian with pale blue eyes and a mole on the side of his prominent nose – one of the foreign auxiliaries who had volunteered to work for the German invaders, either to avoid maltreatment and starvation in a prisoner-of-war camp or because they were Belorussians, Ukrainians, Cossacks, or Tatars who hoped that Hitler would help them gain their national independence.

Alex wore a permanently hangdog expression. The NCO in command of the horse-drawn convoy, Sergeant Behnke, was a bloated-looking man who toadied to officers and made life hell for his subordinates. Quast was incensed to note that he bullied Alex at every turn and persistently addressed him as 'Russian motherfucker'. Although Quast tried to draw Alex into conversation and convey his sympathy, all he got were curt and unyielding replies. And so they jolted along in silence, side by side beneath a mantle of gently falling snow. Then Alex started to sing to himself, very softly, and Quast's mind went back to the days when he and his fellow *Pimpfe* had sat round the campfire, raising their voices to the evening sky and feeling the woodsmoke sting their noses. Something of his mood must have communicated itself to Alex, who gave him a sidelong glance. On impulse, Quast stuffed a pack of cigarettes into the Russian's pocket, suddenly moved by the fate of a man who would have to quit his native land with the Germans rather than be captured and shot by his compatriots.

It was still snowing when they pulled off the road and prepared to spend the night in a handful of peasant cottages. The drivers huddled in the lee of their carts and wagons, pin-points of light from their cigarettes hovering like fireflies in the leaden grey twilight. They were quickly allotted their quarters and hurried inside to glean what warmth they could. Quast deposited his G Pack against the mud wall of Behnke's cottage and pressed his hands against the stove, which had just been lit. Beside him, the sergeant was swigging at a bottle of vodka with his legs apart and his head thrown back. He reeked of sweat, liquor, and nicotine. Magnanimously, he proffered the bottle to Quast, who declined.

'Too good to drink with me, eh?' Behnke's voice was tinged with menace.

'A tipsy signaller wouldn't be much use to you, Sergeant.'

Behnke left it at that, but the look in his eye suggested that he had recognized Quast's pretext for what it was.

Half an hour later the door burst open. Preceded by a flurry of snow, a corporal entered gripping Alex by the collar of his long driver's overcoat. The Russian's face was deathly pale.

'Nabbed him just in time,' the corporal announced. 'He was heading for the woods.'

Behnke, already drunk, savoured his moment of triumph. 'Well, you Russian motherfucker, how about that! You couldn't even give us the slip in a snowstorm, you're so god-damned dumb.'

Alex said nothing. Behnke deliberated, slowly and malevolently, with satisfaction written all over his face. Then he gave a complacent grin. 'So Auxiliary Leskov tried to desert, did he? Fine, fine, this is a job for the MPs.' He turned, still grinning, to Quast. 'Signaller, you deal with him. Take this motherfucker down the road to the nearest provost post and hand him over. He's done for – I can see him swinging from a tree already!' He broke off and eyed Quast suspiciously, then turned back to the corporal. 'Send another man along with them, Karl. Better safe than sorry.'

The track, which ran parallel to the main road, was rutted and knee-deep in snow. On either side, trees jutted darkly from the tangled undergrowth. Their faces swam in the gloom like pallid moons. Alex trudged along in the middle of the track. Three paces to his left and rear came a young private who kept glancing nervously at Quast. An unblooded replacement, he was trembling with cold and agitation and holding his rifle awkwardly away from his body. Also to the rear but on the right, Quast held his own rifle cocked and ported.

They walked for twenty minutes. Quast was determined to gain time and just as determined not to be used as a stooge, least of all by a man like Behnke. On the other hand, he knew he mustn't let the Russian escape or

Behnke would take it out on him – Quast. How Alex must hate the man, he thought, to risk deserting to the partisans. Still, Behnke's outfit was short of drivers – he'd heard the sergeant say so himself. Wouldn't he be as relieved as anyone to see Alex back on the box next morning?

Quest called, 'Halt!' The Russian complied without turning round, his head hanging low. 'Alex,' he went on in a low but incisive voice, 'if you run, we'll shoot. So don't try it, *ponimayesh?* Then you can sing me another song tomorrow morning, *khorosho?*' Alex didn't answer, just nodded apathetically. Had he understood? The young private hadn't understood a word. 'I'm going up to the road to see if I can find a provost post,' Quast told him. 'You keep an eye on this man, understand? If he takes off, shoot him.' The youngster fidgeted with his rifle and stared at Alex's back.

Quast plodded off, then turned and looked back. The other two were standing motionless. From the road came a roar and rumble of traffic. He ducked behind a tree and checked his watch. 'Alex,' he muttered, 'if you make a false move now . . .' Minutes crawled by. He watched the unending stream of vehicles on the road, heard drivers cursing, gears grinding, horses snorting. Peering between the branches, he could still see the two figures on the track below. 'Alex,' the youngster kept saying, 'stand good and still, Alex, or I'll have to shoot you. Please, Alex . . .'

When a quarter of an hour was up, Quast came blundering through the undergrowth and reappeared on the track. 'No luck,' he panted. 'I couldn't find an MP anywhere. We'd better go back. It'll be pitch-dark soon.'

Alex stared at him through narrowed eyes. The youngster nodded eagerly. Then they plodded back the way they'd come. Raucous voices were issuing from the sergeant's billet by the time they reluctantly neared their overnight quarters. A sentry sheltering beside one of the parked wagons said quietly, 'He's roaring drunk again, the stupid son of a bitch.'

Behnke was perched on the table, bawling a song and beating time with his vodka bottle, which was empty. Two equally glassy-eyed figures were lolling against the tiled stove. Four more soldiers lay sprawled on the floor, wrapped in blankets, their heads pillowed on their packs. The low-ceilinged room smelled even worse than before.

'Afraid we didn't manage to unload him, Sergeant. Still, you are short of drivers, and – '

'Screw Alex! I don't give a damn about that Russian motherfucker – tell him to feed the horses and watch his step in the future. As for you, you snake in glasses, piss off – get out of my sight!'

Quast picked up his things and found himself another billet. He heaved a sigh of relief. So that was the going rate for a human life. One bottle of vodka, and a petty megalomaniac forgot he'd meant to murder someone . . .

Dawn had broken. Quast was riding pillion behind a dispatch rider with his pack and radio stowed in the sidecar. The Assault Battalion had recalled him. Slowly, they puttered along the horse-drawn column, which was just getting under way. Alex's eyes lit up as they passed. He raised one hand. Quast touched the rim of his helmet in farewell.

18

AUTHOR: *Hadn't you expected it to be more glamorous, going into action with the Assault Battalion?*

QUAST: *I'd stopped expecting glamour long before. If the rifle companies weren't wiped out, that was the best we could hope for.*

AUTHOR: *But didn't it blight your idealism?*

QUAST: *No. I was far too tired to be emotional.*

AUTHOR: *Mentally tired?*

QUAST: *No, physically. We seldom got a good night's sleep. Lack of sleep makes you apathetic. You don't have the energy to spare for any great mental exertion.*

At nightfall, the Battalion moved into a village at the southern end of Lake Chud. The men were hardly in their billets when an alert came through. Robot-like, they stubbed out their cigarettes, rolled up their blankets, and struggled into their winter battle dress. Then they picked up their arms and equipment and clambered awkwardly into the waiting trucks. Before long, the one-and-a-half-tonners were on their way to the front. Everyone was dog-tired. Barely a word was uttered above the drone of the engines – only an occasional oath or growl of protest when some driver failed to avoid a pothole.

Quast was drowsing. The word 'Abisha' kept running through his head. It sounded like a girl's name, he thought. Actually, it was the name of a shell-blasted village outside Pskov, the major rail and road junction. Overlooking Abisha was Hill 556, and he knew from

Werner that Pskov would be 'gravely threatened' unless 556 was held – the C in C had said so himself. The road they were travelling was the road to Abisha.

The men advanced in extended order. Quast, who was used to the weight of a G Pack, plodded along like an automaton. It was bitterly cold, but the bulky camouflage suit conserved his body heat. From time to time, stray Russian shells smacked into the open ground, sending up clouds of snow and chunks of frozen soil. One of them blew the roof off a cottage not far ahead. Thatch and roof timbers sailed through the air in slow motion. The riflemen in the front rank slowed and started bunching. Quast could hear Düsterhen saying, '. . . lovely firm tits. Panting for it too. It was hell saying good-bye to her.' Men fresh from furlough daydreamed instead of keeping their wits about them, he reflected. Düsterhen had better watch out.

They filtered through a group of buildings, still in extended order, and emerged into the open ground beyond. The plain was now broken by gentle undulations. When a battery of self-propelled guns came rumbling and squeaking up behind them, their arrival confirmed the rumour that had previously run the length of the ranks. It took the form of one word: counter-attack.

The guns halted and the men were told to lie down – a general precaution only, because the dead ground hid them from view. Mortar bombs were landing on the ridge ahead but not beyond it, and small-arms fire was whining high over their heads. Quast took cover in a gulley beside one of the self-propelled guns. The armoured skirt suspended from its flank was scored and dented in countless places, and the rubber-sheathed bogies resting on the track, level with Quast's eyes, were pitted and scarred. Two riflemen flopped down in the snow beside him and lit cigarettes in the lee of the steel colossus. At first he didn't listen to their conversation, but then it sank in. He could hardly believe his ears. They were discussing geraniums and phlox, annuals and perennials, window boxes and roof gardens. Were they trying to exorcize their fear, he wondered, or was their sangfroid authentic?

He tried to gauge what lay in store. They would be counter-attacking over unfamiliar, snow-covered terrain. Not far beyond the ridge lay Abisha, with Hill 556 a handbreadth to one side. This was where the Russian attack had run out of steam – for the moment. Thick veils of powder snow were steadily reducing visibility. It was 5 A.M., the lousiest time of day. Everyone shivered in sullen silence, yearning for warmth and repose. The battalion had been subjected to two months of harassment, dismemberment, confusion, and bloodletting. Their new CO had joined them only a few days before. They still didn't know what to make of him. There was a world of difference between fighting a delaying action and masterminding a counter-attack in the dark. Was he experienced and judicious enough, this tight-lipped young cavalry captain who wore his crumpled cap at a jaunty angle and nervously chewed on a dead cigar? Quast had butterflies in his stomach.

The assault guns' engines roared into life. Quast's limbs were chilled. He struggled to his feet, the G Pack feeling three times its normal weight. They approached the ridge at an angle. The forward command post lay in a gulley that had once been a neatly revetted trench deep enough to conceal a man standing erect. The dugout itself was a cramped, shallow shoebox. Beneath the roof, which was flush with the frozen ground, runners and signallers were huddled together in a heap, rather than seated side by side. Half dug in to their front was an abandoned quadruple pom-pom surrounded by dead bodies and open ammunition boxes. The route to the village was littered with more snow-covered corpses, Russian and German, some sprawled across each other. To the rear, the ground behind the gulley sloped away to a broad, featureless plain bounded on the west by the shores of Lake Chud and on the south by a belt of forest that could only just be seen through flurries of snow.

The artillery observer was zeroing his battery in. Crrump! Clods of earth spurted into the air ten yards behind the dugout. One of the worn-out ten-point-fives had fired too short. From his post beside the entrance, the CO said gruffly, 'Signaller, send: CO to all rifle companies, essential maintain contact.' Quast heard him swear under his breath. 'If the Ivans spot any gaps, they'll give us a bad time.' A fine start to the day . . .

The minute hand of Quast's army-issue watch crept past the hour hand. It was 5:30 – zero hour. The self-propelled guns moved off. Far to their rear, field artillery and heavy mortars opened up. Stiff-jointed with cold, the rifle companies scrambled to their feet. On either side of the command post, men from No 3 Company clambered over the snow-covered corpses on the lip of the gulley. Ammunition belts rattled in their boxes. A hoarse voice penetrated the mush in Quast's earphones. It was No 2 Company. 'Contact with No 1 lost. Visibility poor. Resistance light. Out.'

A mobile assault gun trundled across the dip. Its driver yelled encouragement to the escorting infantry. 'Stay close!' One of the riflemen shouted back, 'Sure, who wants to get his head blown off?'

The snow was getting thicker. Russian MGs hammered ponderously away, submachine guns rattled, high-explosive shells burst like aerial torpedoes. Then an antitank gun joined in. The ten-point-five with the worn barrel was still pasting the slope to their rear.

Sepp, the CO's personal runner, came blundering down the steps. 'Signaller, all companies to watch their flanks and maintain contact. No 3 Company, close up. The Ivans are attacking the western edge of the village.' Ah, thought Quast, a counter-counter-attack . . .

Now the Russian gunners let fly. The bunker started to lurch and sway. As always when a barrage was in progress, eardrums fluttered and lungs were assailed by shock waves. 'No 2 Company calling,' the hoarse voice said again. 'Pinned down. Contact with No 1 lost. Reception very poor. Switching to Morse. Acknowledge. Over.' Quast acknowledged and switched over, and there was No 2 again. 'Enemy breakthrough on left flank. QQQ.' Nothing more, just mush.

From outside a crescendo of small-arms fire mingled with Russian cries of '*Urrah!*' Tracks rattled and engines roared. The assault guns came racing across the dip to the rear, out of ammunition. Quast pushed his helmet and headset back and wiped the sweat from his brow. '*Urrah! Urrah!*' They could hear the chorus on both flanks now. Heinz Müller glanced at Quast under his helmet rim. Quast took a stick grenade and thrust it into the headset compartment of his G Pack. He unscrewed the cap and shook out the china knob on its detonating cord. Müller was also fumbling with a grenade. Quast propped his rifle against the wall and patted his pouches. The rounds inside jingled.

Somebody sprinted overhead, panting and cursing. Fritz tumbled down the steps and landed in a heap. 'Tank dead ahead!' he yelled. Then the entrance went dark. Engines blared and tracks squeaked like a thousand pieces of chalk on a blackboard. The tank had mounted the bunker roof and was turning: left and right, left and right again. The roof timbers creaked, groaned, and splintered, but they held. Quast peered out and up: rivets, bolts, bogies, torsion bars as thick as stove-pipes, track members as bulky as cookhouse loaves, steel plates black with oil and covered with dents and scratches. The forty-five-tonner was right overhead. He'd always dreamed of knocking one out; now he was cowering beneath one armed with a puny rifle and three grenades. He fell back, deafened. The tank had fired an enfilading shot along the gulley. Sand trickled through the bunker roof and misted the air. They coughed, knuckling their eyes. Then the entrance went light again.

The dull grey of dawn was slowly becoming tinged with

the palest imaginable blue. It had stopped snowing. Where were the Russians – what had happened to their infantry? The din of battle was just as intense. No 2 Company radioed: 'All officers killed. Enemy second wave has broken through, heading for command post.' Gingerly, Quast put his head outside. The trench was full of men from No 3 Company, some wounded, some dead. Beside the entrance, two snipers were squinting through their telescopic sights. 'I'll take the one on the left – the one in the fur cap.' 'Fine, the other one's mine.' Two shots rang out almost simultaneously. 'Bull's-eye!' Quast's earphones started cheeping. 'No 2 calling. Breaking through to No 1. Taking up all-round defensive position.'

The tank raced back, precisely the way it had come. Quast caught a momentary glimpse of the rusty towing eyes on the front, the bullet-scarred curve of the armour-plated shield protecting the driver's position. The vehicle ground to a halt overhead, turned, fired along the dip, turned again, and clanked off with its exhausts bubbling. Then the Russian infantry arrived. Guttural cries, bursts of submachine-gun fire, groans, curses in German and Russian, the crack of exploding grenades – all hell broke loose. Quast and Müller stood in the entrance, head-sets off, rifles at the ready, G Packs within easy reach.

They could hear Russian voices overhead. Hand grenades out, cords pulled, count one-and-twenty, two-and-twenty, three-and-twenty, and – because they were so close – four-and-twenty. One pace forward, then lob. The things were up there on the roof. Two reports in quick succession. A hoarse shout in the distance: 'The CO's been hit!' Then another voice, crisp and incisive: 'Everyone obey my command!'

A bloodstained figure slid over the parapet and landed in the entrance well. It was Lieutenant Wille, the mortar platoon commander. 'Shoot me,' he whimpered. 'Don't leavs me lying here – for God's sake shoot me!' A runner materialized on the steps and started to haul the dying man inside. Quast waved him back – they wouldn't have room to move if it came to a fight – but the runner, whose name was Karl, bundled Wille into the dugout and tore his jacket off. Within seconds, he was up to his elbows in blood. Then the whimpering and groaning stopped: Wille was dead. Karl draped the sodden jacket over his face.

Fritz, wide-eyed with terror, shouted, 'Let's blow up the sets and get out of here!' Müller said, 'No, hang on, not till the Ivans come knocking at the door.' No 2 Company called again. 'EB, EB,' Quast signalled back, 'Wait. Out.' Removing his safety catch, he climbed the steps. A burst of submachine-gun fire ripped into the balk of timber above him. He ducked. Then the pandemonium died away. With a backward glance at Müller, he crawled to the surface. The sergeant followed him up.

The sky looked wonderful now – a soft, rich blue with isolated puffs of cloud drifting across it like swans on a lake. The Battalion's tin identification pennant stood out against it, leaning over at a crazy angle. Alongside, with his back against the side of the trench, sat a sergeant. He had a hole in his forehead and a pistol in his lifeless hand. The snow had been trampled into a mush that ranged in shade from palest pink to deepest crimson. Lying near the bunker entrance was a baby-faced Russian whose eyes stared vacantly at the sky. Herbert of No 3 Company lay sprawled across him with one arm bent back. His up-turned palm was full of bright red blood. Other corpses were strewn along the trench, some like solitary sleepers, others locked in a lethal embrace. Among them, half covered with a waterproof cape, was the CO. The trampled snow was littered with weapons, ammunition boxes, helmets of German and Russian design, items of personal equipment. Neatly propped against the wall beside the bunker was a rifle with a discoloured bayonet. Blood was dripping from the bunker roof.

A handful of men from No 3 Company – scarecrows in

torn and filthy camouflage suits – were crouching in the dip. One of them turned, eye sockets and stubble standing out blue-black against the parchment yellow of his face. He signalled to Quast to keep down, then put a finger to his lips and nodded in the direction of the next dogleg. Quast crawled over to him.

'They're just round the corner,' the man whispered.

'And in front?'

'You bet.'

'What about over on the right?'

'Thirty yards of trench, that's all we've got.'

'Terrific.'

'Sure, it's a laugh a minute.'

The artillery observer, who was standing beside the bunker with his powerful binoculars levelled, continued to relay information to his battery in an unruffled monotone. 'Two enemy tanks sighted on western edge of Abisha.' Did that mean the Russians were about to renew their attack? It was high time to put Division in the picture – they'd never break out of the pocket unaided – but it didn't matter how often Müller sent his call sign winging through the ether: still no response. Although shells from the ten-point-fives periodically whistled overhead on their way to Abisha, they did nothing to restore morale.

The men crouched there, dispirited. In the lull that followed the latest salvo, Müller said, 'Why in hell don't those lousy Stukas ever show up? I'm going to radio for air support.' Paul said, 'You're wasting your time.' Still no response from Division, but Müller sent the message anyway, then repeated it.

Paul shook his head. 'You're crazy, Heinz. There aren't any Stukas left – only in newsreels. If they really get that message they'll think we're nuts.'

'Well, aren't we?' growled Müller.

They all fell silent. The artillery observer looked in. 'Message for Battery,' he told his radio operator. 'One tank burning, the other immobilized. Crew seen to bail out.'

But Battery didn't acknowledge either. Nobody spoke. One Russian tank more or less – what difference did that make now? Then they heard the distant hum of engines: aero engines. Everyone crowded outside. There they were, high up in the blue – Ju87 Stukas. Three, six, nine, twelve of them peeled off sharply to the right and swooped like playing cards spilling from a deck. With their gull wings, slender fuselages, and shark's-mouth air intakes, the powerful machines flung themselves into a screaming, almost vertical dive. Over in Abisha, light anti-aircraft guns began to chatter. Then came a series of monstrous explosions. The ground shook. Columns of oily black smoke went up, lit at the base by darting flames. The Stukas levelled off and roared overhead at a mere fifty feet. One pilot waved, another punched the air with his fist. The silence that followed was deathly. It was ten minutes before the Russians slowly resumed firing.

They all squeezed back inside the bunker. The dive bombers had taken some of the pressure off, but they cherished no illusions. The rifle companies were still pinned down by enemy fire. Their hedgehog positions were like islands in a Russian sea.

Hans, who had been sitting there white-faced and silent, suddenly spoke. 'Why not call it a day?' he said in a shaky voice. 'We've had it anyway. Let's go out there with our hands up. Half a chance is better than none.'

They stared at him mutely, stricken by the sight of his ashen cheeks, trembling lips, and dilated eyes. Knowing him, they knew how unflappable he usually was.

'Don't worry, Hans,' said Müller, 'they'll get us out. The Stukas came, didn't they? Division won't leave us in the lurch.'

Hans gave a sob. 'Who have they got to send?'

No one could tell him. For the next fifteen or twenty minutes, all was as quiet as a normal afternoon in some normal sector of a static front line. Their hopes were just beginning to revive when disenchantment struck: a shell landed full on the trench. The dugout was so crowded that Quast barely had room to operate his microphone switch Another shell, this time on the bunker roof, drove the air from his lungs and stabbed his eardrums. Suddenly the barrage lifted. Müller peered out the door, then turned He was very pale.

'This is it,' he said in a low voice. 'They're taking us in the rear.'

They rushed outside with their rifles and grenades Dark figures in camouflage suits were making their way across the seeming infinity of open ground behind them – line upon line of infantrymen advancing in exten ded order, five yards apart. But what were the Russian gunners up to? They'd lifted their barrage to the plain itself! Mushrooms of smoke, clouds of snow, and geysers of earth were springing up between the oncoming figures Although some lay still after every shell burst, the rest closed up and maintained formation. They were Ger mans! The men in the trench stood transfixed. Paul said 'It's just like a movie. All we need now is a heavenly choir . . .' He had a point, thought Quast. Whoever the new arrivals were, Frederick the Great would have been proud of them.

Several hundred men were trudging across the plain under heavy shellfire. Knee-deep in snow and flat as a pancake, the ground made every step an effort and prevented them from advancing by stages, alternately sprinting and taking cover. They couldn't even be certain that the edge of the plain was still in friendly hands, but they had to reach their objective before dusk or risk being pinned down overnight in exposed and unfamiliar terrain They were under orders to abandon their wounded and leave them to be tended by the handful of medics who, far to the rear of the advancing riflemen, darted from one casualty to the next. Only one thing mattered: to plug the gap in front of Abisha and relieve such members of the Assault Battalion as still survived – and this they were

194

doggedly doing, with their limbs still bloodied and be-
grimed from their last engagement.

Now they broke into a run. The first of them came
panting up the slope and staggered into the gulley held by
No 3 Company. A few made their way down to the
command post while the rest charged breathlessly on.
Quast found himself staring into a haggard face framed by
a steel helmet. The man's camouflage jacket was open at
the neck. His insignia were unfamiliar.

'Waffen SS, Police Division. We're taking over this
position. Where's your commanding officer?'

Quast indicated the bloody bundle beside the entrance.
'He's dead, er . . .' He glanced at the unfamiliar badges of
rank.

'Captain,' he was prompted.

'Dead, Captain. No 1 Company's up front, to the right
of that burning tank. No 2's flanking it on the left. No 3's
here, beside the bunker.'

'Very good, Signaller, carry on.'

No 1 Company came on the air. 'We've been relieved,
and about time too – we're out of smokes. Nos 1 and 2
Companies now withdrawing to area of forward command
post.' Müller removed his earphones and said hoarsely.
'Division says they'll send up some sleds for the dead as
soon as it's dark. We're to go back with them.'

It was snowing again. The grey light blurred every
outline. Not a shot was fired on either side. Voices drifted
across from Abisha, mingled with the rumble of cartwheels and the clatter of equipment. They made their way
back in silence, heads bowed. The sleds were piled high
with dead. The remnants of the rifle companies trudged
wearily along in their wake. By midnight they were back
in quarters. A meal was waiting for them – two portions
per man, because the cookhouse noncoms hadn't figured
on such heavy losses.

Quast had felt uneasy from the start, but things had
gone all right again – this time, at least – for him and

Müller and Karl and Paul and a few others. They weren't hungry. They sat around the table, which was spotted with margarine and rifle oil, by the light of some Hindenburg candles. Müller produced a bottle and they clinked glasses. They thought of their ambitious young CO, of Frederick the Great's grenadiers, and of the dead who were lying out there in the barn, some like torn and tattered bundles, others with the outward serenity of men asleep. Bodo Düsterhen was among them, they all knew that. Whether in fear, rage, or blind hatred, the Russian tank gunner had aimed at his solitary figure and fired, but none of them could raise the energy to tell his friend Sepp, who was standing outside the hut, peering into the darkness in the belief that Bodo had merely become separated from the rest and would soon show up.

19

AUTHOR: *Didn't you sense how callous people had become over the years?*

QUAST: *People are callous by nature. In times like those, the veneer cracks. It isn't always pretty, what shows through.*

AUTHOR: *What did you detect in yourself?*

QUAST: *Abject fear. All my self-assurance had gone. That was when I began to grasp what keeping a stiff upper lip really means.*

They buried their dead next morning. They'd eventually had to tell Sepp that his friend was among them. Sepp dismissed the idea.

'He dived into a foxhole when the tank showed up – I saw him heading for it.'

'But Sepp, he never got there. Somebody beat him to it.'

'I just don't believe you.'

'Sepp, pull yourself together. Here he is.'

There lay the remains of a human being. The face was unrecognizable, the chest ripped open, one leg torn off at the hip, one arm missing.

'And you say that's Bodo? You're crazy!'

With a grimace of distaste, Sepp knelt down beside the thing that had once been a young man. He tugged at the trousers until he exposed a pocket and felt inside. When he withdrew his hand, he was holding a cigarette case – Bodo Düsterhen's cigarette case.

They carried out the body of a corpsman, a sergeant of

about thirty. It was riddled with bullets – they counted twenty-three, though none had touched the head. There was a letter in his pocket. The woman's handwriting was ill-formed, with lines that trailed down towards the right-hand margin. 'I think you're right,' she'd written. 'We've grown apart, and the children never see you anyway. You've picked yourself a nice soft job, being a medic – they say those nurses are very accommodating. Me, I'm stuck here at home, and Mother's got her cough back.' Quast studied the dead man intently. His expression was relaxed and peaceful. He'd never have to explain anything to his wife again or feel bad about the children – or listen to Mother coughing.

They decided to send his wife the wedding ring. They felt it was important, after reading the letter, but it wouldn't come off. 'We're not burying him with that ring on his finger,' said Gottfried, with a meaningful look at Dribaschewski, known as Driba, a stevedore from the Hamburg docks. Driba nodded and felt in the pocket where he kept his clasp knife. They turned away. A moment later, Driba said, 'Here, now you can have it.'

Had he been scared? Quast was sitting in the *banya*. The rest were already outside in the snow, but he enjoyed being alone in the heat. He filled his lungs with resinous woodsmoke and stared at the wall. Well, had he? Of course he'd been scared – scared to death – but never really petrified. There'd always been an undercurrent of hope, an irrational certainty that nothing would happen to him. Would it always be like that? The hot stones sizzled as he spat on them. He dashed outside and threw himself into the snow. His body steamed. He felt so alive he could have shouted at the top of his voice: 'Vera, Tonya, Lena, where are you? Here comes Herbert Quast!' That night he got drunk.

Brilliant sunshine was streaming down from a blue dome of sky. The one-and-a-half-tonners had borne them swiftly to their destination along a smooth asphalt road. On the way, they'd passed a sign saying 'Irboska Base Hospital'.

'One little bullet in the right place,' Müller said pensively, 'and you'd be tucked up in a nice white bed.'

'Sure,' said Quast, 'with a harem of nurses and three hot meals a day. What's the matter, Heinz, been listening to too much Russian propaganda?'

Everyone laughed, and Müller said, 'You just don't have the right psychological approach to this war – not serious-minded enough.'

They took up their quarters in some houses scattered around a road junction. One ribbon of asphalt skirted the bank of a river called the Velikaya. The other met the riverside road at right angles and crossed the Velikaya by way of a trestle bridge, a tall, spidery structure with stacks of spare timber lining its approaches. Once across the river, the second of these arterial roads plunged into a belt of forest whose extremities were lost in mist, upstream and down. Distant gunfire rolled through the trees, suggesting that the Russians were determined to capture the road junction and establish a bridgehead south of the river.

Eight men from the signal platoon had been billeted in a house overlooking the bridge. They were standing at two small windows, watching supply columns rumble across it, when a sudden roar of aero engines came from the forest. Everyone stampeded for the door, eager to take cover on the far side of the house. Rather than add to the snarl-up in the doorway, Quast crouched down below the window sill. Then curiosity got the better of him. Peering over the sill, he saw four fighter-bombers with red stars on their wings come streaking out of the forest and point their noses at the bridge. Flames flickered along the leading edges of their wings, and bombs fell away. Tracer from some light anti-aircraft guns beside the bridge stitched delicate patterns in the sky and rose to meet the attackers. Cowering figures leaped from the supply trucks, one of

199

which was already belching smoke. Planks blasted from the roadway went sailing through the dust- and smoke-laden air. Cannon shells pitted the wall of the house which trembled under the impact of a near miss, and plaster trickled from the ceiling. The Ilyushins pulled up their wings and fuselages catching the sunlight as they banked away. The trucks on the bridge came racing down the ramp, one of them wrapped in flames. The driver jumped clear just as it exploded with a muffled roar. And then, as abruptly as it had begun, the nightmare ended. Two bodies lay sprawled on the splintered roadway. Stretcher-bearers ran towards the bridge, followed by engineers carrying tools and lengths of timber. A mushroom of smoke dispersed and drifted slowly down river.

The other signallers filed back into the room, breathing hard and patting the dust off their uniforms. Quast, who was still at the window, felt suddenly sick with fear. For the first time ever, he'd been deserted by the notion that nothing could happen to him. He was just another insect on the face of the earth, waiting for a giant flyswat to descend.

'My hero!' Müller said behind him. 'Honestly, Herbert, this isn't a movie.'

'I know,' he said, and turned away.

Smoke, flames, and a haze of spent explosive. Vast tracts of snow sprinkled with craters. Farmsteads surrounded by clumps of tall trees in whose lee nestled armour-plated monsters with their gun barrels raised. Floating above the skyline, a strip of blue-green cloud fringed with orange by the afterglow. Dwarfed by this panorama, the clustered or isolated dots that represented German infantrymen.

Quast and Brinkmann had been detailed to join the remnants of the rear guard, who were forming a defensive line. A corporal from the combat group they'd been attached to was showing them the way up front. An office hurried past, map case flapping. He hailed their guide. 'So that's where you are. Come on, I need you.' Then he turned to the other two, 'You'll find your way all right.' Moments later, they were on their own.

Dusk fell quickly. The afterglow faded and the shadows turned to indigo. It was quiet apart from some sporadic small-arms fire. The thunder of artillery had abated. They picked their way cautiously between a barn and a dilapidated cottage. A voice from the bowels of the earth said, 'Hey, watch where you put your clodhoppers!' A rifleman folded back the shelter half draped over his straw-upholstered foxhole. He was having a snack – a slice of bread washed down with a swig from his canteen. There was something almost cosy about the spectacle.

'Are you with the Luftwaffe Field Division?' Quast said.

'That's right.'

'We're looking for Combat Group Balthasar.'

'You'll find what's left of it straight ahead, up there by the *banya*.'

'Thanks.'

The shelter half closed again. They heard a rustle of straw and a gurgle from the canteen. Brinkmann, a gaunt Berliner with curly hair and soft brown eyes, said, 'Almost as good as dinner at the Adlon!'

There was the bathhouse with a light anti-aircraft gun alongside, its barrel pointing at the sky. In front of them, a broad expanse of snow littered with corpses. The parapet of the trench looked singularly uneven. Inspecting it more closely, Quast saw that it was topped off with more bodies – German infantrymen, all with their backs to the enemy. 'Did they panic?' he asked, but the company commander, a stocky, hollow-cheeked, stubble-chinned lieutenant with a Russian submachine gun and a P38 in his belt, didn't reply. The niche he allotted them had to be cleared of dead first. He also assigned them a guard of two riflemen, because Russian combat patrols had taken to

201

infiltrating the trenches under cover of darkness. Their escorts, silent and grey-faced with fatigue, simply rolled the unwanted corpses over the parapet.

Quast and Brinkmann draped a shelter half over their recess in the trench. The sentries stationed themselves a couple of yards away. One slept while the other peered into no-man's-land. Mortar bombs came fluttering over – harassing fire only. Reception was loud and clear. Quast went outside to pump the sentries for information and found them both asleep. He shook one of them awake – 'Some protection you are!' – but the man just blinked and grunted. He was too tired to answer.

Quast rejoined Brinkmann and lay down beside the radio. Moments later, a near miss drove the breath from their lungs and tore the shelter half to shreds. The G Pack's dials read zero. A jagged hole had appeared in the side of the casing. Brinkmann said calmly, 'Well, that's that.'

'The radio's a write-off,' Quast reported. 'I'm going back to Battalion to pick up another. Signaller Brinkmann will stay here.' The company commander adjured him to be back by daybreak. He set off at a trot, breathing steadily to conserve his energy. His off-white camouflage suit must have shown up in the darkness, because a machine gun started chattering on the Russian side of the line. Fire away, he thought. In this light, the odds against being hit were a thousand to one, but he put on speed just the same.

Outside the shack was a tumbled heap of straw, and on it lay an olive-drab figure wrapped in blankets and whimpering softly. The door was so low that even Quast had to duck as he entered. The windows of the small, square interior had been tightly boarded up. A squad of infantrymen had lit a fire in an old oil drum and were sprawling around it on the floor. Smoke filled the room from waist height to ceiling and was slowly drifting out the door. They couldn't use the stove. If the Russians spotted smoke coming from the chimney, the place would be flattened in no time.

Coughing, Quast inquired the way to Battalion and asked about the figure in the straw.

'An Ivan left behind by a combat patrol. Stomach wound.'

'Aren't you sending him back?'

'No point; he'll snuff it any minute.'

Quast went outside and bent over the dying man, whose face was a pale grey blur against the blankets. He laid his hand on the cold, moist forehead. The Russian whispered something unintelligible. Quast knelt down beside him. '*Da, da*,' he said, '*khorosho*.' The night sky enclosed them like an inverted bowl. Far above, an aircraft droned solo across it.

The sun was over the treetops by the time he reached Battalion Headquarters. He wasn't to go back, he learned. The Battalion was being transferred, and Brinkmann would be returning with the runner already dispatched to collect them both. Müller, who had saved Quast a piece of smoked meat, ladled some stone-cold bean soup into his mess kit. He sat in a slit trench, munching a slice of bread with his meat and canned soup. It only occurred to him then that he hadn't eaten for at least twelve hours. A shell ploughed into the trees every few minutes, but not with any definite intent. The Russians were ranging on the edge of the forest, not aiming at the command post itself.

He perched on the lip of the trench. German and Russian fighters were wheeling in the sky not far from Battalion's cluster of dugouts. He idly stirred the contents of his battered mess kit, then laid it aside. He could feel the sun's warmth through his quilted jacket. His hands were red now, not blue and frozen. The cold had ceased to torment him. He lay back and stared at the sky. One of the fighters streaked like a hornet across his field of vision, trailing a plume of white smoke. Russian or German? He didn't care. Let someone else sweat for a change – he needed a break. Still, if he were a Russian observer . . . He tried to imagine the view from above: the edge of a forest and, facing it, a broad expanse of open ground. At one particular spot, tracked vehicles, wagon wheels, and human feet had left a multitude of imprints in the snow. If I were a Russian, he thought, I'd clobber this area. I'd guess it was the site of a command post or the route to some kind of headquarters . . .

There was a sudden commotion. The relief battalion's advance party had marched in: eighteen-year-olds laden down like pack mules with belts of ammunition round their necks and stick grenades in their boots and belts. One of them asked if he could make himself comfortable in Quast's trench. He grinned and nodded. The youngster stretched out with a sigh of relief. So did some of his equally footsore companions. Leather creaked and bayonets clanked against gas-mask containers. Quast was dog-tired. He turned over to give his back a share of the sun and closed his eyes. A picture of Vera took shape in his mind – or was it Tonya, or Lena? He dozed off.

20

AUTHOR: *So then you got to feel the consequences of your patriotism – physically, I mean . . .*

QUAST: *I still do, whenever the weather changes.*

AUTHOR: *Did it teach you anything?*

QUAST: *It was a painful experience, but that's no reflection on patriotism. There's nothing shameful about love of country. What was shameful was its exploitation by the megalomaniacs who ruthlessly consigned us to hell.*

AUTHOR: *Were you aware of that at the time?*

QUAST: *No, just amazed at the extent of human endurance.*

Was it really possible to live through such an awakening? To open your eyes and look your own death in the face? Could pain be so excruciating that, instead of feeling it anywhere in particular, you were solid agony from head to foot?

He was lying on his back in a trench. Clods of earth pattered on to his body, sand rained down, cascades of black dust descended. His eardrums still vibrated to the howl of aero engines and the roar of exploding bombs. He'd felt as if a wild beast were gnawing at his elbow, his wrist, his shin, when the machine-gun bullets raked his body. He was paralysed with shock and unable to move. Furnace heat, arctic cold, dull blows, cruel knife thrusts, wet and sticky limbs, a parched and gooey mouth, a throat constricted with nausea – each sensation merged and mingled with the rest. Quast had ceased to think.

Müller's face appeared above him, pale and distraught. He pointed to his helmet, which seemed to have been jaggedly parted along the crown by some demented barber – pointed to the slit in his green head protector and the hair that protruded from it like a pair of cockscombs. Müller had been lucky when the fighter-bombers launched their attack.

'I couldn't find you,' he gasped. 'Everyone else in the other trench bought it – nothing left but bits and pieces. How did you get here? It must be all of ten yards. I thought you were a goner, I thought – ' His expression darkened suddenly. A rifleman ran past. Müller grabbed him by the arm. 'Here, lend a hand – quick!' Quast tried to read the sergeant's face as they lifted him out, but Müller avoided his eye. They laid him down beside the track and opened his uniform. Squinting along his body, he saw nothing but blood.

The hipbone was exposed. The hip itself looked like raw steak. Blood was welling from it. A young medical officer came over. Müller asked him something. The medic shook his head and grimaced. Müller had tears in his eyes. They plugged Quast's wounds with gauze and gave him a shot. Then they pinned a piece of paper to his open jacket. 'Abdomen', it said in big letters. Quast could read it quite easily. He had a vision of the Russian in the heap of straw. It was twelve hours since the soldier in the smoky shack had said, 'He'll snuff it any minute.' But Quast didn't want to snuff it; he wanted to live, and not just for a minute.

Müller had laid a hand on his forehead in farewell as they slid him into the ambulance. Now they were jolting along a corduroy road. Unbeknown to Quast, they crossed the Velikaya bridge. There were four stretchers in the narrow vehicle, two up and two down. One of the men below moaned incessantly. Quast's companion in the top tier was a colonel, the commander of the relief battalion. His face was very pale. He clenched his teeth and stared fixedly at the roof. A splinter had ripped his stomach open.

They'd given Quast a shot of morphine. He felt as if he were stuffed with sawdust, but he desperately strove to assess his chances. Just before being wounded he'd eaten meat, soup, and bread: that was bad. He'd been bandaged up at once: that was good. It would be better still if he got to a hospital promptly, but if not? That would be bad. If they operated on him right away, that would be good, but he was still in transit. What about the planes that had strafed them? Would they finish him off? He drowsily debated these questions while bombs exploded near the road and the ambulance rocked in their blast. The pain was less intense but constant.

They must have driven for at least three hours before the ambulance came to a halt and the doors swung back. Two men peered inside. Quast screwed up his eyes, dazzled by the light. 'Well, he's still alive,' said a voice. Then, 'This one isn't, though.' Metal runners squealed as the stretcher below Quast's was removed. Another voice said, 'Hurry it up, we're pulling out soon.' The men reappeared with another stretcher. Its occupant had his arms thickly swathed and a stand-up collar of bandage round his neck. He was breathing stertorously. More metallic squeals as the stretcher slid into place. A voice beside the ambulance was saying '. . . headfirst into the bread oven when those goddamned bombs started falling!' Roars of laughter. 'Got a cigarette?' The doors clanged shut. Footsteps receded. Boots crunched on gravel; the driver was doubling back to his cab. His door slammed and the engine started up. The ambulance moved off with a jerk. Quast could feel the morphine wearing off.

It was dark when they lifted him out. Squat thatched cottages lined a village street glistening with hoarfrost and pitted with fresh craters. They loaded him on to a hand-cart and wheeled him over the bumpy surface. Suddenly, something came roaring and whistling overhead. 'Bastard!' yelled one of the corpsmen. 'There he is again!' They abandoned the handcart and flung themselves to the ground. The cart tipped up, leaving Quast with his head in the frozen mud and his feet in the air. Bombs exploded, splinters whirred, debris came pattering down. They righted Quast, wheeled him over to a brick building – possibly a schoolhouse – and carried him up three steps. They were inside a light trap. One of the corpsmen fumbled with a blanket draped over the inner door.

Quast heard a noise. A hacksaw, he thought – no, something bigger. Then the door opened. He was looking at a cross section of a human thigh, bone in the middle, blood vessels oozing. The surgeon laid his gleaming saw aside. An assistant in a long, bloodstained apron carried the severed limb into the background. The warm and humid room reeked of disinfectant. Instruments clattered. Quast could hear subdued voices saying unintelligible things. A doctor with hard, weary eyes regarded him intently, examined his wounds, felt his pulse.

'Forget about the rest,' he said. 'Let's concentrate on the abdomen. That's what matters most.' Although the words weren't meant for him at all, Quast nodded vigorously. 'We'll fix him up with a catheter. I want to see if his bladder's intact.'

Passively, Quast let it all happen. Then the doctor bent over him. 'That's the most we can do for you here. The rest'll be up to a base hospital. You're tough enough, my friend – you'll pull through.' *Was* the doctor his friend? Quast felt instantly convinced of it, he was so faint and so racked with pain.

His stretcher had been deposited on the floor of a farmhouse kitchen. Now there were two slips of paper on his jacket. He ground his teeth at being left to lie there when every minute was precious. A sergeant came in with two orderlies at his heels. They inspected the slips of paper pinned like price tags to the supine figures on the floor. The sergeant pointed to Quast and three others. 'Shove 'em in the first one.' Quast was picked up, carried outside, and slid into an ambulance. The engine throbbed, the gears and transmission whined. More jolting, more groans – another eternity of sound and movement. It was late at night when they unloaded him. Another bare room. Again the stretcher was deposited on an expanse of rough floorboards. He tossed his head from side to side, the pain had become so bad.

The room was dimly lit by one weak bulb – emergency lighting only. Quast thought he was alone until he heard a rasping intake of breath nearby. Then a muffled voice said, 'Hey, you!' Craning round, he saw a head swathed in bandages with big dark stains on them. He couldn't discern any eyes.

'Yes?'

'Where were you hit?'

'Stomach – and other places. How about you?'

'Shot in the back of the neck.'

'How come?'

The head looked like an outsize ball of soiled cotton in the half-light. The voice that issued from it was a muffled monotone. 'They overran our position at dawn. Somebody fell on top of me – dead. When I wriggled out from under, this Ivan was looking down at me. *Idi syuda*, he said – come here. They yanked me out of the trench. One of them went on ahead while the other walked behind me. Then the one in front came round behind me too. They made me clasp my hands on top of my head. After a while they lost their way and got mad. Then they started talking together, very quietly. The sun was up then.' The man's breath rattled in his throat. 'Next thing I knew, one of them rammed his gun against the back of my neck and pulled the trigger.'

'And now you're here,' said Quast.

The muffled monotone continued. 'I lay there thinking I was dead. Then I heard voices. I could feel the sun on my face. I opened my eyes but I couldn't see a thing, just blackness. All at once someone said in German, 'This one's still alive, let's take him along.' It was one of our reconnaissance patrols.' Another rattle in the throat. 'But I still can't see a thing – not a thing.'

Quast made no comment. What could he say? They lay there in silence, each imprisoned in his own world of pain.

The walls were tiled, with a key pattern at eye level. The light was bright but not dazzling. He was being given a blood transfusion. The orderly administering it was a Russian of about forty, a dark man with a lined face. Quast felt quite light-headed. He addressed the Russian with a kind of bravado: 'What's this, Ivan – helping a goddamned fascist?'

'My name is Andrei,' the Russian replied in guttural German. 'And you are only a trainee fascist – a little one, that's all.' He smiled. 'You're in luck. The operating room was closed, but for you, little signaller, all lights on. Are you really a general in disguise?' Andrei undressed him with deft, gentle hands and eyed his wounds impassively while Quast just lay there, unable to associate such butchery with his own flesh and blood. Then he said, 'So, now I'm going to shave you. Let's see if you've a few more hairs on your belly than you do on your face, *molodyets*.'

They rolled him back and forth on the operating table like dough, debating such topics as angles of penetration and intestinal sutures. 'All right,' said the surgeon, 'now start counting.'

'Yes, sir. One-and-twenty, two-and-twenty, three-and-twenty . . .' he was just about to throw the grenade when he lost consciousness.

There were crisp white sheets on the bed. The hospital was Irboska Base Hospital. They'd driven past the signpost three days earlier, not that Quast could remember. He lay there racked with fever, thickly bandaged from breastbone to thigh. He head was bandaged too, and one arm had been splinted. They'd also sewn up the superficial

210

wound in his leg. He had a raging thirst. He pictured a wooden bucket suspended above a Russian village well. He saw its ice-cold, crystal-clear contents, saw it spill over, saw long skeins of sparkling water.

The next bed was occupied by a man with a pale, strong-featured face, a tangle of dark beard, and friendly eyes. 'Thirsty, eh?' he whispered. 'You mustn't drink, though. It'd kill you.' Tactfully removing his tumbler from Quast's line of vision, he moistened a scrap of gauze and gently dabbed his parched lips. Quast snapped at it, but the bearded man said, 'No biting, lad!' The bearded man was almost immobilized himself by a terrible wound. 'They shot my ass off,' he explained. He had an artificial anus in his belly. It stank when the orderlies lifted the bedclothes, but the whitewashed room stank anyway. Vomit, pus, excreta, disinfectant – Quast learned that human beings could be degraded by sheer stench, but he also learned that Christian charity could flourish in such surroundings. The bearded man watched over him constantly. If the bedclothes slipped off his mutilated limbs, he summoned an orderly. If he arched his body in pain, he gently restrained him. If he smacked his parched lips like a fish out of water, he reached for the little gauze swab.

The colonel died one night. They'd operated on him twice. He lay quite still in the bed at right angles to Quast and the bearded man. Quast could see his face in profile. His ears grew steadily whiter, his cheeks fell in, his eyes sank deeper into their sockets, his lips became thin and waxen.

While Quast was hovering on the brink of sleep, uproar broke out in the ward next door. First a Russian voice, then a German: 'You *kaputt! Nix voda!*' A Russian with a stomach wound had drunk from a washbowl. He died towards morning.

Quast was transferred to another ward. As they carried him out, he looked back at the bearded man and tried to smile encouragement. The bearded man said quietly, 'Get well soon, lad.' Then he glanced down at himself and shrugged. His lips were pale and his eyes bright with fever.

Quast's new bed was up against a whitewashed wooden partition. A bug crawled out from between two planks. Revolted by the sight, he crushed it to death. 'Hey, bug-killer,' called a voice from the bed opposite, 'what's your name?' Quast had just been given a shot. Now that the pain had eased, he suddenly felt flippant. 'Joseph Vissar-ionovich Stalin,' he said. 'Stick that in your pipe.'

They all burst out laughing. It was an eerie kind of laughter – halting, breathless, agonized. There were six men in the bare white room, none of them fit to travel or they'd have been sent home long since. They weren't supposed to laugh – laughter might burst a blood vessel or snap an elaborate suture – but they laughed anyway.

The doctors came in and removed Quast's dressings, inspected his hip and the fresh red scar that now ran down his stomach. They looked him searchingly in the face, checked his temperature and pulse chart, and filed im-passively out. One of the theatre orderlies stayed behind to renew his dressings. 'You've lost a yard of gut, but don't blame the surgeon. He sewed you up like something out of a textbook. Blame someone else for what's miss-ing.' He jerked his thumb heavenward and departed with a cheerful wave. The door closed behind him.

They lay there quietly, all tucked up and attended to. 'Well,' said Quast, 'so I've presented the Führer with a yard of gut.' His next-door neighbour tittered. 'That ought to please him, with everything so scarce these days . . .' The laughter went on and on. In the exhaus-ted lull that followed, they heard the plip-plip-plip of something dripping on to the floor: blood. Three minutes later, Willi was whisked away to the operating room. Franz said, 'Let's hope he hasn't laughed himself to death.'

Every day, the sergeant cook came to Quast's bedside

212

and asked what he felt like to eat. He never asked the others. Quast supposed the cook must have a soft spot for him, but he didn't know why. Not being hard to please, he seldom thought of anything fancy. After a week, the cook's moon face peered amiably round the door. Quast was about to speak when the corpulent sergeant forestalled him. 'Congratulations, you aren't a celebrity any more.' Seeing Quast's puzzled frown, he went on, 'The boys who look as if they're going to kick the bucket, the way you did a few days back, they get some decent grub before they go. Now that you're off the danger list, that's it.'

A month later, he travelled back to Germany in a hospital train. The more serious cases made an intermediate stop at the transit hospital in Insterburg. Quast was dumped on an examination table and had his dressings changed by a plump, fair-haired nurse. 'Well, well,' she said as she removed the last of them, 'isn't that something!' He was suddenly surrounded by three young women, all gazing down with sympathetic interest at his nether regions. He saw sparkling eyes, parted lips, soft dimples, stray curls, taut blouses, hips swelling under striped skirts. He saw dainty ears, downy necks, slender fingers, the shimmer of blond hairs on rounded forearms. Spellbound, he followed the girls' sure and supple movements.

He could sense the healthy bodies beneath their rustling aprons – feel the smooth skin and play of muscle. He was lapped in warm voices, long-forgotten verbal melodies. All the desire, all the craving for human contact that was in him clamoured to express itself. And there where the nurses were so tenderly unwrapping, swabbing, dressing, bandaging, and strapping him up, something occurred whose significance he had never fully appreciated until his encounter with Lena in the deserted cookhouse. But here, at this of all times?

213

He felt his face flush scarlet, but the girls just grinned. Then one of the trio laughed out loud. 'That's my boy,' she said. 'Always keep your end up – life looks better that way.'

21

AUTHOR: *You didn't have a lot to do with girls?*

QUAST: *I had too many things on my mind. To me, women were beings from another world.*

AUTHOR: *You mean you were indifferent to them?*

QUAST: *Far from it. I felt there must be at least one sphere of existence where sympathy and understanding reigned – in other words, the world of women, which was so remote from me. But as for love, what did I know of it?*

AUTHOR: *Couldn't you have played the lady-killer – the scalp-hunter?*

QUAST: *I was too scared of hurting someone.*

By midsummer, Quast was back with his mother. Although he still paid daily visits to the hospital to have his dressing changed, he could live at home as an out-patient. They'd had to operate on his stomach again, to remove a splinter from one of the grenades worn, they guessed, by the boy who'd been torn to pieces beside him, and his thigh refused to heal. He had a limp, but he'd been able to discard his crutches. He also had a permit exempting him from wearing a belt.

He didn't enjoy going out. It embarrassed him when people in streetcars stood up and offered him their seats, so he preferred to brave the pain and walk. One day, while hobbling down the street, he ran into Hotte Schulz, a school friend from Berlin.

Hotte, who was also on convalescent leave, had been invited to help judge a Hitler Youth athletics match.

Quast accompanied him to the stadium, where he envied the agility of the youngsters exerting themselves in the spacious arena. It was like a flashback to his school days, except that he now found himself as out of tune with the Hitler Youth leaders as they were with him. Listening to their speeches, he wondered how anyone could string so many platitudes together in so short a space of time. The whole thing was eyewash.

One brown-shirted official, a twenty-five-year-old whose callow face was alight with self-importance, tried to shoo him back to the stand when he joined in an argument over whether a long-jumper had overstepped the board. 'You, there! Yes, you, soldier boy! Scram!'

Quast, who looked like a raw recruit in his baggy uniform, had draped a rug round his shoulders to keep off the drizzle. Already in a belligerent mood, he failed to grasp that he was being judged by outward appearances. He saw red. 'I'm surprised you don't feel ridiculous, standing there with a tape measure in Germany's finest hour. Is that how you expect to win the war? What are you doing here anyway? I thought your kind were crying out for combat duty.'

The official was speechless. The bystanders murmured angrily. 'For God's sake shut up,' said Hotte, and drew the official aside. Quast heard, 'Head wound, got to make allowances . . .' He felt sick.

Later, Hotte talked him into going to a café – 'Plenty of skirt there!' – but he felt more out of place than ever. The small talk repelled him and the smoke-laden air made him hoarse. A shrill-voiced blonde with greasy hair and no forehead sat down beside him. She asked for a light – leaned forward and put her hand on his thigh. Quast said, 'Keep your paws to yourself.' Starved of fresh air, he got up and limped out without saying good-bye to Hotte.

He could have played the cripple for months and cultivated some passing fancies at the same time; that he realized, but he somehow felt worthy of better things. He resolved to get back into shape, or as near it as he could manage.

Every day after having his dressings changed, he retired to the hospital basement. There, at the end of a passage overhung by a maze of heating and water pipes, was a big, cool room with a linoleum floor and a ping-pong table in the middle. It was much frequented by convalescents, who went there, like himself in search of exercise.

Today there was only one, an Austrian colonel in the Waffen SS. His glum expression vanished when he saw Quast. 'At last!' he barked, limping briskly over to the table. 'I was beginning to think none of you idle bastards would turn up.' He certainly needed the exercise, Quast reflected – he couldn't even stand without swaying. The colonel had cold, bright eyes and a lean face that looked sick beneath its veneer of suntan. His mouth was scarred in a way that gave him a permanent sneer. He didn't look much like a good Samaritan, thought Quast – not the sort of man to cross swords with.

They tightened the net, selected two scuffed old bats, and checked the balls for cracks. The colonel had first serve, but he put his bat down on the table.

'Tell me, Signaller, what do you make of this assassination attempt?'

Today was July 30. Ten days earlier, Colonel von Stauffenberg had tried to blow Hitler up in his own headquarters. Quast parried the question.

'Well, you can look at it two ways, ideological and technical.'

'Forget about the ideological angle, Signaller. Treason's treason – or it is if it doesn't come off.'

Quast didn't answer. The conspirators' motives were far from clear to him. They couldn't have been out for power alone. Most of them were highly decorated, highly intelligent men who could easily have gratified their

217

ambitions without resorting to a *coup d'état*. There must have been something else behind it, but what?

'All right,' the colonel persisted. 'What about the technical angle?'

'Technically speaking,' said Quast, 'it was a pretty feeble effort.'

'You can say that again. They ought to have left it to us in the Waffen SS. Some conspiracy! When I think how we handled things in Austria before the Anschluss . . .'

'Mm,' said Quast.

'You can't run a revolution without getting your hands dirty. Think of it: they actually selected a man with one good arm and one good eye, and he had more guts than the rest of them put together. As for the others – pah! They couldn't even explain to the country what it was all about. I tell you, the Army's a broken reed these days.'

Infuriated by this absurd generalization, Quast flung his bat down. If the arrogant bastard wanted to sound off, he thought, let him do so to the local branch of the National Socialist Women's Association.

'All right, Signaller, simmer down. Just take a look at those generals of yours. First they underestimated the Führer and thought they could ditch him when he'd served his purpose. Then they came to heel and excused themselves by quoting their oath of allegiance. In the meantime, they've shown they don't know much about their trade.'

'Come on,' said Quast, 'you can't write them off just like that.' But the colonel had the bit between his teeth.

'Listen, Signaller. When winter comes, even the daftest parents wrap their children up warm, right?'

'I guess so.'

'You see! The generals didn't even do that. What happened outside Moscow in forty-one? What about Tikhvin and the Demyansk pocket? Or Velikiye Luki in forty-two? It was the Russians who had the fur jackets and felt boots, not us. It was our MGs that jammed, not theirs.

218

The generals underrated them. They couldn't even read a weather map.'

'What do you mean, no fur jackets?' said Quast. 'There's plenty, but who's got them, the Army or the SS? Anyway, since when have your kind worried about the Army?'

The colonel screwed up his eyes and served. Quast got the ball back with difficulty, but the colonel flubbed his heavily sliced return. The ball rolled under the table and came to rest at Quast's feet. He bent down and retrieved it.

'We've been worried ever since ten days ago,' the colonel said grimly. 'That's when a few of your officers and gentlemen did their best to blow the Führer up – or had you forgotten?'

'There's nothing wrong with my memory,' said Quast. 'I can also remember when the generals got Knights' Crosses and field marshals' batons and so on, and the Führer shook them gratefully by the hand. I always thought he meant it.'

The colonel gave an impatient grunt. 'You don't understand. Every donkey needs an occasional carrot. Come on, your serve.'

But Quast persisted. 'Who ordered our boys to march on Tikhvin and the Valdai Hills and Stalingrad and the Caucasus? The Führer – the Supreme Commander, I mean.'

A dangerous glint came into the colonel's eyes. 'The Führer was wrongly advised,' he snapped. 'He can't run the war single-handed.'

'No, but he'd like to – and he's always said the Bolsheviks are useless. After all, they taught us in school that the Germanic race is superior to the Slavs.'

'So it is. You only have to look at them.'

'Oh, I have! I don't see much difference, if you take the Russian guard divisions, or the Siberians – or the Cossacks, or the Georgians.'

'Every country has its crack troops, Signaller.'

'That's just what I'm saying.' Quast served.

The colonel sent back a scorching return that missed the table.

Quast laughed. 'But we're short of territory,' he went on. 'Our nation needs the East – the Führer says so himself.'

'Well?'

'Well, he must have known in advance he couldn't rely on his generals. If so, why did he march on Russia regardless? Wasn't it a little bit risky?'

The colonel looked at him sharply. 'Not as risky as what you just said, Signaller.'

Quast got the message. 'I'm only asking,' he retorted. 'You're welcome to supply the answer, Colonel.'

'You think you can say such things and get away with it?'

'As long as I say them to men who've served in Russia.'

The colonel laughed, baring his teeth as if about to bite. Quast took advantage of the drop in temperature to say, 'Try to see it from my angle, Colonel. I mean, there we are in Russia, where the Führer wanted us, and we can't even fill our mess kits because of partisans, and because vehicles get bogged down in the mud and locos freeze up. We didn't reckon with Stalin organs either, nor fighter-bombers and T34 tanks, nor with the fact that the Russians love their country.'

'I already told you, man: Blame the generals!'

The ball flitted back and forth across the net a few more times, but neither of them felt like playing any longer. They bade each other a frosty good-bye. The colonel wanted it every which way, Quast told himself as he hobbled off down the street. If something went right, the Führer could take the credit. If things turned sour, the generals were at fault for obeying him. And if they stopped obeying, then they were doubly to blame. Where did the truth lie? Was the oath of allegiance valid, or wasn't it? Was absolute obedience right or wrong? Where was the dividing line between discipline and stupidity?

After the attempt on Hitler's life, the Nazi salute was made compulsory for all branches of the armed forces. Raising the right hand to cap or helmet became a thing of the past. Outpatients were ordered back to barracks. Quast packed up his traps and went. He'd been posted to Gniezno. The name struck a chord in his memory: Boleslav I, King of Poland, had been crowned there in 1025, after a triumphal journey from Polish Kiev, Gniezno Cathedral was nearly a thousand years old, yet the Party hacks kept blathering about Polish racial inferiority. They didn't have much sense of history.

The company was housed in a hutted camp. The beds were hard, the meals almost inedible, the men's spirits at rock bottom. One evening, Quast and a few companions arrived back at the main gate after a listless stroll through town. The sentry let everyone pass except Quast, whom he asked to show his papers. An official spot check, or plain bloody-mindedness? Quast didn't care which it was. 'Screw yourself,' he said, and walked on. The sentry, an elderly private with close-set eyes, unslung his rifle and levelled it at him. Quast said, 'Put that thing away. You can hardly lift it – and besides, you'd fall on your ass if it went off.' The guard commander came doubling out of the guardhouse. 'Sergeant,' said Quast, 'tell this member of the master race to put his popgun away. He thinks I'm a Russian in disguise.' The sergeant bawled him out. 'Look, Sergeant,' he said politely, 'you're getting me all mixed up, shouting like that. I always thought we were liable to get shot if we tried to escape from this establishment. Me, I'm trying to get in.' The sergeant made a note of his name and unit.

Lying on his bed that night, Quas realized that he had to get away. What did this comic-opera outfit have to do with defending the Fatherland? The whole feel of the place was wrong. The Russians were deep inside the Baltic States again, knocking on the gates of Warsaw, threatening the borders of East Prussia and Slovakia. All over the eastern provinces, trucks were being loaded with furniture from the homes of Party officials. Leave, he told himself. Go where the real soldiers are – where people don't kid themselves and can still depend on each other.

Next day, the company commander asked him not to be a nuisance. 'It only makes paperwork,' he said, 'and I can't abide the stuff. Anyway, I'm just as sick of this place as you are.'

The girl was truly lovely. She was lying asleep on a bench in the local park. Her hair was blue-black, her lashes were long enough to cast shadows on her flawless cheeks, and her lips were red and full and ever so slightly parted. She was wearing a simple dress of some coarse material. One strong brown hand kept hold of a straw purse, one leg was slightly flexed. Her thighs were firm but slender. Quast stood there on fire. It was like a fairy tale, he thought. He felt he must be dreaming. A bee droned past. The summer breeze that stirred the linden leaves smelled sweet and heavy.

The girl opened her dark eyes and regarded him serenely. He sat down on the bench at her feet and said, 'Pleasant dreams?'

She blinked a couple of times. 'I wasn't dreaming of a fairy prince, that's for sure, and you don't look like one anyway. Not in that uniform.'

'Pity. I thought I'd found myself a Sleeping Beauty.'

The girl smiled. Then she sat up and brushed a strand of hair out of her eyes. 'What's your name?'

'Herbert. What's yours?'

'Irina.'

'Where are you from?'

'I came here with a trainload of evacuees from Odessa. Would you like to see our farm?' She took a worn leather

222

wallet from her purse and produced a photo of an avenue of tall poplars with a white house at the far end.

'A palace,' he said. 'So you are a princess.'

She laughed. 'There are lots of big farms in the Ukraine. It's a rich country.'

'Homesick?'

'Yes.'

'Where are your parents?'

'Mother's dead. They took Father away in 1939 – we've never heard a word from him since. My brother Valerian was deported back in 1937. Internal exile, they called it.'

'Why?'

She shrugged, staring up at the trees. 'My brother Yuri's a soldier now, in Germany. I'm being evacuated to the Reich.'

Quast said, 'Irina, I'm due back to camp, but I'd like us to meet again.'

Her reply was matter-of-fact. 'So would I. This evening at the station – that's when our train moves on. Seven o'clock, all right?'

'Fine,' he said. Then he bent down and kissed her on the nose.

She didn't move, just sat there looking up at him. 'You're more brassy than you look.'

'And you're as sweet as a honeypot.' Quast turned away quickly. He had to get back to camp to see Captain Scherbaum.

Ten minutes later he was standing in the captain's office. Scherbaum was a thin, pallid man with a small head and horn-rimmed glasses. He had an artificial arm ending in a black-gloved claw that protruded menacingly from the sleeve of his uniform jacket. A buzzer sounded, and Scherbaum removed the receiver of the field telephone from its mottled brown Bakelite box. Quast stared out the window. A drill was in progress down below in the square. Some forty- to fifty-year-olds were learning how to stand at attention, right face, left face. They were too fat, too

223

stiff, too ungainly, too short-winded: willing but unable. At the moment, they were straining to ensure that their feet formed an angle of eighty degrees, neither more nor less. Quast big his lip and turned away. The captain replaced the receiver.

'Signaller Quast, we're taking you on as an instructor.'

Quast looked incredulous. 'For that bunch down there?'

'Yes,' the captain said sharply, 'for that bunch down there.'

'As of when, Captain?'

'You start tomorrow morning.'

'No, Captain.'

'You refuse to obey an order? I don't have to tell you the consequences.'

Quast nodded towards the window. 'Honestly, Captain, see for yourself. Left face, eyes right, eyes left – God Almighty, is that what we're hoping to win the war with?'

'I'm forty-five myself!'

'You're an experienced soldier, Captain, but those men down there . . .'

'What are you getting at?'

'Well, imagine those men on the Eastern Front. Imagine them under attack by Suvorov graduates, all over five feet ten, or a guards division – soldiers trained to wield a rifle and bayonet like a bricklayer handles a trowel. Think of those poor devils then, standing there with their feet at eighty degrees. They wouldn't know what hit them.'

'Signaller Quast, come to attention!'

Quast stood still, knees braced, chest out, stomach in as best he could, shoulders back, thumbs aligned with trouser seams.

Scherbaum cleared his throat. 'I formally place you on detachment. You'll take up your duties at 0800 tomorrow.'

'No, Captain,' Quast retorted. 'I formally volunteer for reassignment to the Assault Battalion, northern sector.'

Silence. Words of command came echoing up from the square. 'You knock-kneed old women,' bellowed an

224

instructor, 'I'll have you drilling on your stumps by the time I'm through!' Quast looked at Scherbaum and raised his eyebrows. The captain stared moodily at his desk. All at once, he smiled and put out his good hand. Quast shook it.

'All right, Quast, point taken. If that's the way you want it, lots of luck.' Scherbaum paused. 'You've no idea how I envy you.' The black leather claw made a fleeting gesture.

Two hours later, Quast was on his way to Poznań to catch a glimpse of his mother and an early-morning train for the front. Ah, Irina!

22

AUTHOR: *First you argue with an SS officer. Then, a little later, your comrades express burning hatred for the Führer and icy contempt for Party officials. Politics had reared its head again. Didn't that make you think?*

QUAST: *Not the way you mean. I was a soldier by then, not an overgrown member of the Hitler Youth. I sensed there was something rotten about the system – something we'd have to change once we got home. But as for thinking it out, I didn't have – well, the leisure, if you like.*

It was still dark when he left the house at 4 A.M. His mother hadn't bewailed his departure, hadn't questioned the need for a soldier who couldn't even wear a belt and bayonet to go back to war. He was grateful to her. He hadn't had to explain how wretched and forlorn he felt among joyless people who all had something to hide: grief for the dead, uncertainty about the missing, anxiety about relatives in areas threatened by bombing or invasion, fear of prosecution for black marketeering, indignation at the callous treatment of Poles with whom they'd long been on friendly terms, adulterous wartime affairs, doubts about the point of fighting on, impotence in the face of circumstances they'd never wanted but tolerated for far too long. More and more as the days went by, Quast had felt himself suffocating in a world of shadows.

His mother stood at the garden gate in her threadbare dressing gown. He could see, by the fitful moonlight filtering through the clouds, that she had tears in her eyes. Kissing her, he said, 'Go inside, it's cold. And don't worry.' But when he turned to give the small, shivering figure a farewell wave, he had a strange sense of finality. If they ever met again, it wouldn't be here.

His footsteps punctuated the nocturnal silence. He was rested, cheerful, looking forward to the journey, and excited at the prospect of seeing familiar faces when he rejoined the Battalion. He was leaving all this behind – it didn't concern him any more. The thought didn't sadden or distress him. He whistled as he went.

The leave train stopped at Memel, the end of the line. If he waited there long enough, he reflected, the war would come to meet him. The personnel forwarding centre gave him a movement order to Liepaja. The platform was crowded with shivering, sour-faced officers and men. They boarded a freight train laden with ammunition and supplies. The transportation officer warned them all to be on their guard. The Russians had broken through, he said, and no one could guarantee that the line was clear. He was only a little premature. The Russians soon reached the Baltic between Memel and Liepaja, cutting the Germans off in the Kurland pocket – or bridgehead, to use the official euphemism. As it was, Quast's train got through without incident.

He was in pain. The wound in his thigh had still not healed, and the dressing was saturated. He asked his way to the hospital and waited in Casualty while surgeons punctured a lung. He didn't watch – the sight of stainless steel biting into human flesh had become too much for him. Then he was standing, half naked, in front of a nurse called Elisabeth, a lithe young woman with a slender neck and wavy fair hair. She frowned when she saw his wound.

'What on earth are you doing here?'

'I've come to rejoin my battalion.'

Her grey eyes were warm. 'Four weeks, that's the most you boys in Kurland can count on, didn't you know? After that you're dead, wounded, missing, or captured. You really want to go up front?'

He shrugged. 'What about you? Why are you still here?'

Anti-aircraft guns were barking and aircraft droning overhead. The windows rattled incessantly.

'Someone's got to look after you boys.'

'But . . .'

'He was killed,' she said, then hesitated. 'You could be his younger brother.'

Looking at her, Quast saw a mixture of sorrow and yearning in her eyes.

'Please stay till tomorrow.'

'Well . . .'

'Don't worry. I'll fix it with the doctor.'

And that was how, the same evening, Quast found himself in a bare little room stacked with blankets. He stowed his belongings under an iron bedstead and stretched out with a sigh, waiting for Elisabeth. His eyelids drooped. The noises in the passage – doors shutting, crockery rattling, footsteps, the squeak of a wheeled stretcher – combined with the extraneous roar of supply columns and tanks to wrap him in a strangely soporific jumble of sounds.

Suddenly, Elisabeth was bending over him. He reached for her and felt the warmth beneath her apron. 'No, not now,' she whispered as he slid an eager hand up her thigh, but she parted her legs an inch or two, and he touched the epicentre of her trembling body. She drew a deep breath and kissed him, then stepped back abruptly. In the dimness, he could see her wide eyes, her half-open mouth, and the strands of hair over her flushed face. She gave a nervous little laugh. 'I only looked in to see how you were. I'll be with you in an hour.' She shut the door quietly behind her. Quast sat up on the hard bed, his heart pounding. Then he lay back and closed his eyes. For all his excitement, he fell asleep again.

228

It was ten o'clock at night when he woke with a start. He felt dopey. Turmoil reigned outside. A confusion of voices and footsteps drifted into his lair. He struggled into his boots and draped his overcoat around his shoulders. Stretchers laden with groaning, moaning figures were being carried along the passage. He made his way to the entrance. Elisabeth was there in a long rubber apron, holding a clipboard. She was checking off names and making notes with tight-lipped concentration. Beside her stood shirt-sleeved medical orderlies and doctors in snow-white gowns whose severity was offset by the cigarettes dangling from their lips. None of them took any notice of the lone soldier leaning against the wall with his coat collar up. Ambulances squealed to a halt, doors slammed, stretcher-bearers called to each other in subdued voices, engines idled noisily, exhaust fumes hung in the air. All the wounded had their heads swathed in bloodstained bandages that gave no clue to the features beneath.

Elisabeth looked up and saw him. Her expression softened, but only for a moment. 'Facial wounds,' she called. 'A whole consignment. We'll be operating all night.' She shrugged and added, almost inaudibly. 'Pity . . .'

Quast gave her a rueful wave. 'So long, Elisabeth.'

Three hours later he was sitting in the back of a truck with some infantrymen, lumbering in the direction of Riga. The main square of Frauenburg was deserted, every window boarded up. He recalled the Baltic Germans he'd been to school with in Warthegau and heard their sing-song voices extolling the beauties of their native land.

The truck dropped them near Riga Station. There was nothing moving on the tracks and no rolling stock in sight but two red boxcars nestling against a bumping post. He made his way to the personnel forwarding centre across a yard enclosed by a sooty brick wall. 'You'll be called,' the sergeant told him. 'Wait in the building over there.'

The building turned out to be a gymnasium redolent of school – of linoleum, sweat, and leather-padded horses. Rifle oil and smoke made their own contribution to this mélange of smells. Long rows of packs and rifles stretched across the floor, and between them were sleeping, eating, gesticulating soldiers, some with the Assault Battalion's emblem on their shoulder straps. Their familiar faces brightened when he waved. They pooled their gear and formed a group, but conversation soon languished. Although there was talk of a breakout to East Prussia, it sounded unconvincing. When a truck arrived to take them to Battalion, they shouldered their packs and boarded it in silence. Quast was glad to be back, but the others' apprehensive faces made him doubt if they felt as he did.

The Battalion was resting. Heinz Müller had been sent home two weeks earlier, the soles of his feet riddled with splinters by a grenade that exploded immediately behind him when he hit the dirt. Quast noticed a lot of new faces. All too often, when he mentioned a name inquiringly, he got a one-word answer: dead, wounded, missing. The signal-platoon commander was delighted to see him again. 'One of the old gang at last!' he exclaimed. Quast felt momentarily puzzled until he realized that the words were meant for him. Then he reported to the battalion commander. Major Karsten was a lanky, red-faced man with silver-blond hair, pale blue eyes, and a beaky nose. Quast took note of the Knight's Cross dangling beneath his cleft chin and the close-combat clasp on his chest. At least he knew his business.

'So you're Quast,' Karsten said. 'I've heard of you. Why are you still a signaller first class?'

Quast shrugged. 'Battalion always had enough on its plate, Major. There wasn't any time for that sort of thing.'

'I see. Well, now there is: I'm promoting you to corporal.'

'Thank you, Major. That's great – it's the best rank bar none.'

'What gives you that idea?'

'You know the old saying: Corporals are the backbone of the Army. A backbone without a head's all right, but you can't imagine a head without a backbone – it wouldn't stay put.'

Karsten grinned. 'That's a bit unfair. Let's call them mutually dependent, shall we? Very well, Corporal, carry on – and congratulations.'

He was really one of the old gang now. The MO examined him with much tongue-clicking and pronounced him unfit to take part in the next operation.

That night, twenty-odd men sat in a cramped little shack getting drunk. Many of them clinked mugs with Quast, but he only took a sip each time. Hard liquor gnawed at his vitals in a way it had never done in the old days. His next-door neighbour was Corporal Wellmann, whose Morse speed never exceeded eight words per minute, even in a crisis. Wellmann wore the Iron Cross First Class. Cut off in an abandoned command post, with a Russian machine gun installed only yards away, he had prevented a breakthrough by calling down fire on his own position. Signaller Dremel, a gruff and laconic Bavarian, was lolling across the table from Quast, quite as drunk as Wellmann.

'Know something, Quast?' said Dremel, less laconic than usual. 'Hitler would be proud of you.'

Quast caught the contempt and belligerence in his tone. 'Meaning what?' he said.

'Well, volunteering for combat duty with half your guts shot away. You really must be a true believer!'

They had to put their heads together to make themselves heard above the surrounding din. Quast said, 'So what do *you* believe in?'

'We don't believe,' said Dremel, 'we know.'

'You know?'

Wellmann chimed in. 'Sure, we know we've got to get out of here. We'll be needed later on.'

231

''Sright,' said Dremel. 'To clean up that brown-shirted shit back home.'

'All those Nazi peacocks in their latrine-coloured uniforms,' said Wellmann, ' – they'll have to go, for a start, the arrogant swine . . .'

The tirade developed into a duet, with Dremel and Wellmann venting their spleen in turn. '*And* the racial fanatics,' said Dremel, '*and* the SS, *and* the Gestapo . . .'

'And the local Party bigwigs,' said Wellmann, ' – the ones who go from house to house with their eyes shining and their bellies spilling over their belts, and ring the doorbell, and shove their arm in the air when the woman answers, and sing out, "Heil Hitler, Frau So-and-So, your husband's given his life for the Führer, you can carve his name with pride."'

Quast was dumbfounded. 'Maybe, but – what about Germany?'

'Here,' said Wellmann. He pulled a Walther magazine from his pocket. '*That's* what we'll use to clean up the place you call Germany. You think those Nazi shits have any connection with Germany – or Prussia, for that matter?'

'What we need first,' Dremel said, 'is a nice, orderly withdrawal, just so we can get home and save what's left of our country.'

'Is that what you're fighting for?' asked Quast.

Wellmann nodded. 'Yes, sonny, that's what we're fighting for – a sane, decent Germany. The same thing my father fought for as a trade unionist.'

'A trade unionist?'

'Sure, and a socialist – *and* he had one of these.' Wellmann tapped his Iron Cross. 'From the first war, but it didn't stop him being crippled for life by the Gestapo and called a stinking traitor.'

Dremel raised his mug to Quast. 'I bet they didn't teach you anything about that at Hitler Youth camp, did they? You've got a lot of leeway to make up. Cheers!'

Quast raised his own mug, dismayed and bewildered. His mind went back to a warm afternoon in the fall of 1932. The fairground booths had been boarded up for the winter, and he'd hidden among them to watch a platoon of Brownshirts practising house-to-house fighting armed with 98K carbines. 'Smoke 'em out, the Red rats!' yelled the squad commanders. When the exercise was over, the stormtroopers formed up, flushed and perspiring, and chanted anti-socialist jingles in unison. And he, secreted in an outsize trash can, had raised the lid an inch and looked on, open-mouthed with awe.

And now he'd been told of a socialist who loved his country, was awarded the Iron Cross First Class by the Kaiser, and got beaten up by the Gestapo. The man beside him was his son, whose hatred of Hitler was as little in doubt as the bravery that had earned him the same decoration. Quast downed the contents of his mug at a gulp.

The din rose to a new pitch. Everyone was shouting at once. Quast elbowed his way outside and stood there in the cold night air, staring into space. Earlier, when reporting to the CO, he'd overheard some officers discussing the situation. 'Things are as lousy as ever, gentlemen,' Karsten had told them. 'But guess what I just got straight from the horse's mouth? – the Führer's headquarters, I mean. We're now using secret weapons – miracle weapons guaranteed to wipe the smile off Churchill's face! You don't think they'd lie to honest German soldiers, do you?' Quast felt more bewildered than ever. Everything had changed. Good guys and bad guys – which were really which?

A sergeant in camouflage jacket and steel helmet ran past, buckling his holster. He wrenched the door of the shack open.

'Emergency! Prepare to move out in full combat order – the Ivans have broken through!'

Quast helped as best he could to sober the revellers up.

The one-and-a-half-tonners were already moving into line. Words of command rang out, muttered oaths mingled with the clatter of weapons and the crunch of boots on gravel. The men clambered aboard, sluggish with drink, and the trucks started up. He watched the convoy until it vanished into the darkness like a phantasmagoria. Then he strolled back down the village street. Next time, he thought. Hanging around in the rear was worse than any combat assignment. A loose shutter was flapping somewhere. He stumbled over a discarded vodka bottle. The breeze smelled of alcoholic vomit.

Two days later they quit the village and headed in convoy for the rumbling, smoke-enshrouded horizon. The oncoming traffic – trucks, jeeps, and horse-drawn supply wagons loaded with panicky haste – had to move aside for them. Soldiers hung in clusters from every vehicle, and groups of civilians trudged past, pushing bikes and handcarts. The buildings beside the road were eerily deserted.

The big farmhouse stood on high ground, roofs well maintained, driveway carefully asphalted, not a post or picket missing from any of the fences. Looking down over the gentle undulations that separated it from the plain below, one could see an idyllic, almost parklike landscape embellished with clumps and avenues of trees, silvery streams, and meandering ribbons of pale grey road. Dark green, dark brown, dull red, ochre – all these colours interacted beneath a sky in which shreds of bluish cloud scudded past.

'Out of the truck and get that gear unloaded. Command post in the drawing room, radio station in the master bedroom!'

Quast was soon seated over his G Pack at an elegant table butted up against a pair of twin oak beds. There were no bedclothes, but plump mattresses covered with floral ticking were a mute invitation to the weary. Fritz lay sprawled across both beds, puffing on an enormous cigar.

Its acrid scent mingled with the all-pervading aroma of hot fat. Potato fritters were in preparation, because the runners' squad had unearthed a store of big yellow potatoes and were grating them at top speed. A voice outside called, 'Hey, who likes pork chops?' A submachine gun chattered, and an inoffensive pig bit the dust.

A battery of heavy artillery came through: 'Our forward observer and his radio operator have been held up. Can we zero in with your assistance?' Quast raised Karl, who had set up his station with the forward platoon, down beside a road junction in the plain. 'Can do,' Karl replied. 'Sergeant Wegener will observe. Where do they want the things to land?' Quast relayed Karl's question to the battery's operator and passed the word forward: 'Bridge this side of main intersection.' Karl's response: 'All right, tell them to fire away.'

A distant report, then a gurgling, slithering sound overhead. Quite suddenly, a big grey mushroom sprouted from the ground in front of the bridge. 'Not bad for a start,' said the voice in Quast's headset. 'Up two hundred, and they'll be smack on target.'

The destruction of paradise had begun.

23

AUTHOR: *Tell me, though – was it really self-defence?*
QUAST: *Pure and simple.*
AUTHOR: *In a just cause, you mean? But did you still regard it as that? What exactly were you doing, up there in the Baltic States?*
QUAST: *Trying to survive.*
AUTHOR: *Honestly? Dashing young Corporal Quast of the Assault Battalion gives a Russian his come-uppance: Isn't that nearer the mark?*
QUAST: *Think what you like. If I hadn't hit him, I wouldn't be here to answer your questions.*

'Quast!'

'It's me, all right, Steckel. How are things with you?'

'Ah, it's a dog's life, boy.' Food, officers, the weather – Steckel could always find something to beef about. When he stopped bellyaching, the outlook was really black.

They were standing outside a barn on the edge of the trees. Although Steckel was due to relieve Fritz at the blocking position in the wood, he lingered, thumbing through the contents of a cheap wallet. 'I'm engaged,' he said proudly, and shoved a photo under Quast's nose. It showed him looking comically, unnaturally stiff and erect, with his flue-brush hair gummed to his head. It was noticeable that he hadn't known where to put his big red hands. Beside him stood a young woman with a spotty face and dense curls. The photographer had at least contrived to preserve the young couple's touching air of innocence. Steckel said, still proudly, 'Her name's Mathilde, but I call her Hilde.' Quast looked first at the picture, then at Steckel. All at once, he felt sick and faint. He looked back at the photo, seemingly enthralled, so as not to have to look at Steckel. He knew, with piercing certainty, that Steckel wouldn't last the day. 'There's no rush,' he said. 'Fritz won't mind waiting a couple of minutes. Let's talk a bit.' But Steckel was adamant. 'Business before pleasure, pal. See you later.' Despairingly, Quast said good-bye.

Two hours later he was sorting out his equipment. An attack was scheduled for next day, so only the barest essentials could be taken. After shaving, he laid out a clean pair of socks, some soap, a can of margarine, a chunk of bread, a handful of toasted croutons, some pencil stubs, and a message pad. Then he heard a voice outside: 'Signaller Steckel's just been killed – the Ivans are pasting the wood!' He had to sit down quickly.

None of them could sleep. They lounged around in groups, playing poker and smoking long, evil-smelling cigars lit with rolled-up rouble bills. The windows were blacked out with blankets and the room was wreathed in sooty candle smoke. When dawn broke, they laid their cards aside. Win or lose, what did it matter?

Communication with the rifle companies was tested and found adequate. The eastern skyline turned pink, then yellow. They went outside. Helmets on, straps down. On either flank, for as far as the eye could see, men emerged from the shadows of the wood, from behind barns and haystacks, banks and hedges, and set off at a slow trot. Only now did their own artillery open up: this was to be a surprise attack.

The ground, which sloped away gently towards the east, was dotted with clumps of bushes. The shadows cast by the morning sun looked long and inky in the crystalline air. Major Karsten, striding out five yards ahead of Quast, tapped his ear. Quast nodded and raised his hand: reception was still good. They ran into some sparse rifle fire. Then fountains of brown earth began to rise in their midst: the Russians had woken up at last. To the right of Quast, a rifleman fell flat on his face. Another folded up and started crawling to the rear. An ammunition carrier halted and dropped his box. Then, clutching his throat with both hands, he collapsed in slow motion.

Having been ordered to cross the flat ground quickly, they made all the speed they could. 'Quast,' Karsten shouted, 'new command post, farmhouse left of bushy-topped tree!' The firing grew heavier, with machine guns joining in. The rifle companies plunged into the scrub and worked their way forward in sudden spurts. Mortar bombs began to fall, concentrating on the first wave. The farm-house beside the odd-shaped oak tree was deserted. Quast put his set on a table. The table wobbled on the uneven brick floor, so he fetched a plate from the kitchen and wedged it under one of the battered legs. Reception remained good. All stations kept their speed high and their messages brief. The firing steadily intensified. A wailing salvo of rockets shook the ground on their left. Quast checked the rifle companies in turn. They'd all reached their primary objectives and were regrouping for the next phase of the attack.

A dark green truck with big Cyrillic letters on the doors came jouncing up to the farmhouse and skidded to a halt. There was a German soldier at the wheel. 'Compliments of the Ivans,' he yelled. 'American job – brand new!' he added, and roared off again with his prize. Quast looked out the window at the peaceful garden – the flower beds carefully mulched with straw, the neat fence, the arbour with the bench in front of it, the wooden shack in which hens were still clucking, the small barn. Suddenly his view was blotted out by a wall of discoloured steel, a massive caterpillar track: a Tiger tank! The commander shouted something to Karsten, who was standing outside. Then the walls trembled as the Tiger's engines blared. It turned on the spot and lumbered off. Quast stared, blinked, and stared again. The peaceful little garden had vanished. Arbour, fence, bench – all were buried beneath the rampart of soil dredged up by the monster's tracks.

The Russians had recovered from their surprise. Fountains of earth continued to spurt from the pall of smoke and haze of spent explosive that hung like a curtain over the company sectors. The command post itself was under heavy rocket and shell fire. By now, the signal section had dug itself in behind the farmhouse, right up against the foundations. The other stations were becoming less and less easy to read, and their 'EB – Please wait' requests more and more frequent. Quast felt thoroughly uneasy. He removed his headset and looked up to see a grimy face under a battered steel helmet. It was Dremel, grinning from ear to ear, with a mess kit in his rugged fist. Carefully, he handed it down into the slit trench. 'Luncheon is served, sir,' he said. 'Care for some fresh chicken soup?' Quast swiftly cupped his hand over the receptacle to prevent any more earth falling into it. So the hens he'd heard clucking in the shack had found their way into a stewpot, even in this bombardment. The farmhouse, which was visible for a long way, had now come under direct fire from a Russian antitank gun. The shells penetrated the front wall and exploded inside, making the radio set jump repeatedly. Lieutenant März dived out a window with his head retracted like a tortoise. Behind him, part of the frontage caved in and collapsed.

The CO continued to pace around outside. Quast saw Lieutenant Holt, the commander of No 2 Company, come sprinting up to him through the dust and smoke.

'We need reinforcements, Major. I'm down to 50 per cent. We – '

'What the devil are you doing here?'

'My runners didn't get through.'

'Lieutenant Holt, a company commander's place in action is up front with his men. I've nothing more to say.'

Holt delivered a smart salute – not of the Nazi variety – and doubled back into the murk. Three months later, he covered the depleted battalion's withdrawal with his company's last remaining machine gun until an anti-tank shell blew him to pieces.

The firing suddenly eased. The companies had dug in, their progress checked by Russian resistance.

When a radio set failed, Quast was sent forward with a replacement. He crawled along a gulley flanked by bushes and birch saplings. The grey G Pack felt heavier than usual. His hip was aching, and his rifle continually caught on roots and branches. The wind whistled in his helmet. He kept his head down, though the machine-gun fire pattering into the bushes above him was unaimed. It came from far away, not from immediately on his left, where the remains of No 2 Company were pinned down in a hollow by small-arms fire. The soil was sticky and smelled of mould. He paused for a moment to catch his breath. When he looked up, his heart stood still: dead ahead, crawling towards him along the same gulley, was a Russian. His helmet was scratched, his uniform muddy, his right hand curled round a rifle with the folding bayonet extended. He paused, too, and raised his head. Quast saw a peasant face with narrow eyes, a broad nose, chapped lips. A bead of sweat was rolling down the man's forehead. His eyes widened, staring straight into Quast's.

They both jumped up, but the Russian was quicker. Hampered by the G Pack, Quast was still on one knee when the Russian took a pace forward with his rifle at the ready. He lunged, but Quast still wasn't on his feet and the blue steel flashed past his right ear. Quast didn't stop to think. His reaction was instinctive, not cool and calculating, his one desire to defend himself and live, not kill or maim. Still lunging with his mouth open and borne along by his own momentum, the Russian overbalanced. His head was now level with Quast's chest. Desperately, Quast brought his rifle butt round and drove it as hard as he could into his assailant's face. There was a terrible, crunching sound. The Russian fell headlong and lay still. His fingers clawed the grass as though trying to uproot it, then relaxed. Quast knelt beside the body, pale and trembling. He was appalled to see a thick red rivulet oozing from under his enemy's helmet. Looking down at himself, he detected splashes of the same red on his jacket and a smear of it on his butt plate. For no very definite reason, he took the Russian's rifle and hurled it, with a convulsive sob, into the bushes.

A salvo of shells forced him to hit the dirt. He lay there, chest heaving and knees trembling, with the smell of the Russian – a mixture of sweat and Lysol – in his nostrils. Then he crawled on, unable to look back. His cheeks were moist and his glasses blurred. Already, it might have been a bad dream, the moment that had taught him the fine distinction between courage and desperation, the workings of chance and the will to live.

He scrambled to his feet and toiled on through brown, knee-high grass. Thirty yards on, at the top of a rise crowned by more young birch trees, a runner came trotting towards him with his head darting from side to side and his rifle at the port. He saw Quast and stopped.

'Careful, Quast, the Ivans are trying to sneak through. You could bump into one any time.' The runner gave a sudden frown and looked at him more closely. The ashen cheeks, the eyes filled with lingering panic, the blood-stained uniform – all told the same story. He gave a low whistle. 'You mean you already did?'

Quast nodded almost imperceptibly.

'And?'

'One-nothing,' said Quast, jerking a thumb over his shoulder.

'Well, I'll be damned!' The runner said no more, just hurried on.

Next day, Quast trudged past the farm where they'd feasted on potato fritters and pork chops. He'd been assigned to the rear guard. Now that their counter-attack had failed, the Kurland pocket was shrinking again. The farm buildings had been burned down. Of the main house, all that still overlooked the shell-pitted forecourt was a single gable end. The fences were smashed and the lawns ravaged by tank tracks. The table Quast had used was in the garden. Underneath, bereft of its sole, lay a discarded boot. The whole place reeked of smoke and ashes.

They'd marched, run, and crawled twelve miles or more by nightfall. Flares soared into the sky beyond the grounds of their latest intermediate stop, a country mansion, proving that the Russians were in no mood to rest. The house itself was surrounded by oak trees. Quast and a fellow signaller named Willi picked their way past some dead horses and went inside. On the ground floor, in the octagonal hallway, some soldiers were warming themselves round an improvised stove. Fluttering from the finely wrought banister rail was a dirty bandage. Quast and Willi climbed the stairs to the first floor and squeezed past some fallen masonry into a corridor with watered-silk walls. Their boots grated on the parquet.

Quast opened a door. 'Hey,' he said, 'a piano!' Willi brushed past him and wiped some debris off the lid with the back of his sleeve. The instrument was still in tune. His fingers flitted over the keys, bearing Quast away on a tide of melody. Moonlight streamed through a hole in the roof, between splintered rafters and shattered tiles, and faintly illumined a young girl's portrait on the wall. The polish on the antique furniture was so rich that it shone through its coating of dust. A salvo of shells rocked the building. Willi suddenly took his hands off the keys.

'Makes you feel mellow, doesn't it?' He sighed. 'Those gunners are getting too damned close. There won't be much left of this place before long.'

From below came the sound of agitated voices and

scurrying footsteps. Somebody shouted for a stretcher-bearer. Somebody else called their names. Still under the same strange spell, they went downstairs.

The trench traversed a gently rising field of stubble that sloped away towards the enemy. On either flank, leafless birch saplings swayed in an autumn wind. Russian gunners were ranging on the field. Their forward observer was obviously lurking somewhere in the belt of forest dead ahead, which protruded into the dark brown landscape like a huge furry tongue. Quast zig-zagged fast across the stubble, periodically throwing himself flat between shell bursts. A final spurt, and he was in the trench. Swearing under his breath, he propped his rifle against the earth wall beside No 3 Company command post and crawled, complete with G Pack, into the little dugout. A lousy position, he told himself. He'd learned to judge a position by its rearward approaches, not only by its forward field of fire. Getting out of here would be a feat of skill as well as a matter of luck. When he went to fetch his rifle, an unwelcome transformation awaited him: his rifle had had a bolt; this one didn't. Someone had swapped them at his expense. Not for the first time, he was unarmed.

Although the Russians subjected the position to heavy shellfire, they didn't charge it. Instead, they went for No 1 Company, which was dug in beyond the beech woods on the left flank. The attack petered out. The Russians had either underrated No 1 Company or were simply probing it in strength.

Towards evening, the order came to pull back. They quietly evacuated the position and tiptoed across the stubble under cover of darkness. After slowly withdrawing for half an hour, they were overhauled by the men of No 1 Company, who had also disengaged with the utmost caution. 'Couldn't bring him with us,' Quast heard one of the shadowy figures say. 'Had to bury him in a foxhole. I brought his papers along . . .'

No 1 Company now took the lead, while No 3 acted as rear guard. Quast had unloaded the G Pack on his number two, a skinny young replacement who regarded him with doglike trust and never strayed from his side. Their feet ached badly after four hours' uninterrupted marching, but the platoon covering the road to their rear reported no sign of the enemy.

An ordnance truck was waiting for them in a farmyard. Quast accosted the armourer sergeant, who was standing on the tailgate issuing ammunition.

'I don't have a bolt in my rifle.'

'Come again?'

'I'm short of a bolt and I need a new rifle.'

'You've lost your bolt? That's a disciplinary offence.'

'Shut up and give me another rifle.'

The sergeant bridled. 'Whether or not you get a rifle is up to me.'

'And whether or not you get out of here before the Russians arrive is up to me,' said Quast, grabbing the hem of the sergeant's overcoat.

'I'll report you!'

'You do that,' said Quast, 'and don't forget to send a copy to the Führer.'

Quast got his rifle. He took charge of it as lovingly as a mother presented with her newborn baby. He withdrew the bolt and inserted a clip. Bolt forward, clip ejected, first round into the chamber. Bolt lever down, safety catch to the right: rifle loaded and secured. He felt happy again.

The rear guard had been given a new commander, a fidgety Signal Corps lieutenant who'd never commanded a rear guard before and didn't know his way around. As he hurried past, nervously inspecting his little band of men, Quast thought of his passage with Lieutenant Ellberg: *They're waiting for orders, Lieutenant, but I don't know what to tell them, because I've never been taught . . .* How long ago was it: ten years, twenty? Little more than two, but it seemed an eternity.

They started climbing through broken terrain filled with dips and clumps of trees that restricted visibility. At the top of the rise, the road skirted a large farm. There they called a halt. Sergeant Wegener and fifteen men were to march another mile to the village where Karsten had set up Battalion Headquarters. The rest would remain at the farm and keep watch. Quast accompanied Wegener to the next bend, where the road swung left between two stretches of forest. They studied the map and strained their ears. A distant hum of engines could just be detected.

'They can't be that far behind,' said Wegener.

'The lieutenant thinks they'll hold off till daybreak,' Quast replied.

They exchanged a dubious glance and shrugged. Quast memorized the route to Battalion Headquarters. He was loath to rely on the lieutenant.

24

AUTHOR: *It really does look as if you meant to play the hero that night.*

QUAST: *You're being deliberately provocative. If I didn't know, I'd say you were looking for a hook to hang your prejudices on. A hero? I'd be sparing with that word if I were you.*

The squat, whitewashed farmhouse stood beside the road. Its four front steps led into a narrow passage. Behind the first door on the right was a small, square room with a tiled stove in one corner. It was still warm, though the fire had gone out. 'For God's sake don't light it,' Quast told his number two. 'The smoke would show up for miles.' They'd put the set on the floor and were lying beside it. The light of the full moon slanted through the window. The lieutenant lay stretched out on an iron bedstead against the wall, snoring. The road was under observation, he'd said, so nothing could happen. 'You really think so?' said Quast, but the lieutenant had already dropped off.

Quast went outside, faced the wall, unbuttoned his fly, and made an ugly stain on the whitewash. Then he heard voices coming from the road. Two German infantrymen were hobbling towards him in tattered uniforms with their feet wrapped in straw. They'd spent half a day in enemy hands. The Russians had removed their boots to deter them from running away and temporarily confined them in the loft of a haybarn. While their captors were getting drunk down below, they'd wrapped their feet in straw,

246

carefully pulled a board out of the wall, and lowered themselves to the ground. They were happy to see another German.

Quast looked incredulous. 'You mean I'm the first one you've seen?'

'Yes. Why?'

'Weren't you challenged by a sentry back there on the road?'

They shook their heads. Quast's uneasiness mounted. What had happened to the lookouts? He woke the lieutenant, who was annoyed at the intrusion and sleepily ordered the two escapers to stay with the rear guard. They muttered rebelliously, pointing to their feet, and hobbled off. The lieutenant just shrugged. 'Wake me in an hour,' he told Quast. 'I'll do the rounds then.'

Quast stretched out on the floor. He proved communication with Battalion Headquarters and gave instructions to his number two.

'Don't switch off, keep calling every ten minutes. Wake me in half an hour – or before, if you think something's up. And stay awake, do you hear?'

He felt sure the Russians would leave them in peace for a while. It was just after 3 A.M., and they'd never been known to pick a fight at this hour. He pillowed his head on his arm, breathing deeply and evenly. Whatever happened now, he'd done all he could.

'*Urrah, urrah!*' The Russians sounded as if they were on the doorstep. Bursts of submachine-gun fire peppered the roof. Quast jumped up, sick with fright. His number two had been fast asleep. The lieutenant slowly propped himself on one elbow. 'Outside, quick!' Quast shouted. 'Take it easy,' said the lieutenant. Quast tapped out their call sign, then 'FGA', the code for 'Enemy attacking', then 'QQQ'. He thrust the set at his dazed-looking radio operator and told him to follow. They flipped their safety catches and dashed outside. The lieutenant was awake at last. He ran after them, trying to button his jacket with trembling fingers. Bullets were whistling down the road. They'd only just rounded the corner of the farmhouse when a couple of grenades exploded inside. Quast looked at the lieutenant, who was peering around him in panic-stricken surprise.

'When I say move,' Quast whispered to his number two, 'take that G Pack and run like hell. Get back to Battalion HQ. We won't be needing a radio here much longer.'

Knots of riflemen had gathered behind a barn, waiting for orders. Taut-faced, they gripped their weapons convulsively. Muzzle flashes were spurting from the base of the fence around the house where Quast, his radio operator, and the lieutenant had just been asleep. Quast said, 'Come on, Lieutenant, let's counter-attack. They're just as scared as we are.' But the lieutenant gave him a bleary-eyed sidelong glance and shook his head, nervously fingering his pistol. Quast swore. All the riflemen had started blazing away at the muzzle flashes. The radio operator was kneeling alongside with the G Pack on his back, gazing up at him like a faithful hound. If I were a Russian, Quast thought . . . He looked left, across the field of stubble that rose to meet the edge of the wood.

And there they were, charging full tilt down the slope. He could make out some thirty dark figures, with more emerging from the trees behind them. 'Get going,' he shouted to his number two. 'Quick, you've got to save that set!' The youngster jumped to his feet and bolted. Quast turned to the rest. 'Look out, Ivans on your left!' Then, happy to be able to do something positive at last, he ran towards the Russians. They looked sinister and unreal, like people in a dimly lit subway or puppets bobbing up and down on wires. He stopped and raised his rifle. The one in front must be an officer, he thought; hit him, and it might take the steam out of them. At the moment, little flames began to dance ahead of the running figure: muzzle flashes from the officer's submachine gun.

Quast was transfixed by a red-hot skewer and hurled to

the ground. As he lay there on his back and struggled for breath – as his mouth filled with blood and the Russians pounded past him, shouting hoarsely – he stared up at the hazy moon and thought, with mild surprise, that this was it at last. He'd known it when he walked through the garden gate, but it was easier than he'd feared.

The riflemen were fighting for their lives. The noncoms had pulled themselves together and rallied their demoralized young replacements. Raucous words of command, grunts of rage and pain, wild yells, muffled curses, the clash of steel on steel, rattling bursts of submachine-gun fire, agonized groans, whip-cracking rifle shots, pounding feet, the dull thud of falling bodies – all became fused into a terrible cacophony. Hand-to-hand fighting raged among the barns and outbuildings. Duels developed between men who had never seen each other before and could scarcely do so now. Locked together in an orgy of mutual destruction, the battling figures surged in every direction, leaving a trail of dead and wounded behind them.

Quast lay in the midst of it all. Calm and composed, devoid of all needs and desires, he waited for the inevitable. Then he heard a voice in his ear: 'Are you still alive?' He nodded weakly, feeling bemused and faintly resentful. He wanted to be left in peace, not pestered by some fugitive from death. Why pick on him? 'I'm going to get you out of here,' the voice whispered. Quast shook his head. Why couldn't the fellow leave him alone? He was dying. He felt as light as a feather – serene and contented. Nothing mattered any more. 'I'll get you out; just relax.' Quast was past resisting. The man gripped his collar and hauled him across the stubble on his back, then dropped to the ground himself and lay flat. Minutes went by. Quast closed his eyes and drifted off. The man took him by the shoulders and rolled him over on his stomach. He vomited some blood. 'You'll have to crawl from here on!' He shook his head, then felt a tug at his sleeve. He crawled. He didn't know he was crawling until he heard the man whisper, 'That's it, keep going.' Now they were lying under a bush. He wanted the torture to stop. 'Beat it,' he groaned. 'Take my paybook and beat it.' They lay side by side, panting.

He couldn't distinguish his tormentor's face – or was it his saviour? 'You go on,' he said imploringly, but the man said, 'Where to? I don't know the way; you do. You'll have to show me.' Quast tried to see the man's eyes, but it was too dark. He nodded. The man hauled him to his feet. He swayed, but the man turned and caught him on the back. 'Along the hedge,' Quast said thickly. The man draped Quast's arms over his shoulders and set off. Quast lost consciousness. When he came to, the man was saying, 'Hey, you! Where to now?' Quast said, 'Leave me, please . . .' He drifted off again, but the man shook him. 'Come on!' Quast said, 'Now along the edge of the wood and across a railroad track – I saw it on the map. Just beyond that you'll find the road to – Oh, I don't know the name of the dump . . .' His voice sounded very far away. Then he heard nothing more.

The man was tottering, staggering along a village street, bent almost double under Quast's weight. He stopped outside the cottage that housed Battalion Headquarters. Quast said, 'Put me down.' His legs gave way, so the man half-carried him inside. The CO was there. Quast tried to stand straight and deliver a report, but no amount of training could help him now. He collapsed. They laid him down on some straw. Karsten said, 'Good God, Quast, you again?' März, the adjutant, smiled. 'Don't worry, lad, we'll get you out of here. The set's back too. We'll soon be listening to the BBC again.'

The submachine-gun bullet had gone straight through him, in below the heart and out beside the spine. They strapped a field dressing over each aperture. By now, bullets were whistling down the village street. März buttonholed two privates who were carrying a box of hand grenades outside. 'Leave those. Just stick a couple in your belt and carry Corporal Quast to the rear – you know where our fallback position is. And don't turn up there without him!' März was out the door in a flash. The two men swore. One of them suggested carrying Quast in a shelter half suspended from a pole, and went to look for a suitable length of wood. Riflemen ran past the window. The firing in the street grew steadily fiercer.

Finding no pole, they manhandled him on to a shelter half and stood looking down at him with undisguised hostility. 'He's through anyway,' said one of the two. 'Let's leave him.' Quast, with his mouth full of blood, mutely shook his head. The other man said, 'Let's try carrying him outside first.' They lifted the waterproof triangle so that Quast half sat, half lay in it with his legs dangling, and staggered into the street. Bullets whizzed past their ears and ricochets whined off the stones. They ran as fast as they could. Beyond the last house, the street veered off and became a sunken road with banks on both sides. Mortar bombs were landing in the hollow. The men hit the dirt. Quast lay there with blood trickling into his collar. His eardrums thudded and his breathing came and went in spasmodic gasps. 'All right,' said the first man, 'let's beat it.' Quast made a supreme effort. 'If it was you lying here . . .' They looked at him wryly, then at each other. Then, reluctantly, they picked up the shelter half and the burden that threatened to cost them their lives. Quast passed out.

When he came to, they were standing beside a small river. The trestle bridge had been blown and was sagging into the water. Waiting on the far bank was März. He looked at his watch and yelled, 'I didn't tell you to stroll it, you lazy sons of bitches! Get moving; the water'll wake you up!' Cursing, they hoisted Quast onto their shoulders and waded across like hunters retrieving the carcass of a slaughtered deer.

The men were lined up on the edge of a wood. Quast was carried past them. Looking up, he saw treetops and a strip of dark grey, rainy sky. Then faces swam into view – pale and drawn, with a smattering of stubble in every shade from black to blond and ginger. The sunken eyes were red-rimmed with fatigue, dull and apathetic or unnaturally bright. The men's collars were open and their woollen head protectors pulled down round their necks. Some had cigarettes drooping from their lips. They grinned under their helmets and made jocular remarks. 'What, going home again? Some guys have all the luck! Signallers always were too lazy to walk. Still got your balls, that's the main thing!' Wellmann said, 'Give the Führer our love. He ought to pay us a visit some time.' They put Quast down. A kneeling aidman gave him a tetanus shot in the forearm. 'Hospital again, eh? You must have a season ticket.'

He was lifted into an RSO, a tracked transporter, and shoehorned in between some empty gasoline cans. They wedged an extra helmet under his chin to keep him from spitting even more blood on to his soggy red jacket. The driver, a bony sergeant, said, 'I'm going to have to put my foot down, Quast; the Russians have this stretch under observation. Hang on tight and cross your fingers for us both.'

It was an agonizing trip. Russian antitank shells whistled past them with a sound like a giant bullwhip. The vehicle pitched and tossed, lurched and swayed. Quast could hear the sergeant shouting and swearing above the tumult. They reached a sunken road, only to be balked by a column of stationary trucks just as it was straddled by some rocket salvos. Quast peered over the side of the RSO, wondering how he could extricate himself if a splinter hit the gas cans and ignited their dregs. The sergeant put his head out the cab window and bellowed, furious at the delay. When he got Quast through to the casualty-clearing station, he picked him up in his arms like a baby and accosted the MO in charge as he emerged from the operating tent to count the wounded men laid out in front of it.

'This one's urgent, Captain. Chest wound – Assault Battalion.'

Which was how Quast came to be slid straight into the field ambulance that had just come lurching up the track. The sergeant raised his hand in farewell. Quast nodded and relapsed into unconsciousness.

Darkness had fallen by the time they deposited him, with thirty or forty others, on the flagstoned floor of a large rectangular room resembling a school assembly hall. It was draughty and filled with the sound of hurrying feet. Somebody called, 'Seen Major Hegemann, 2nd Battalion of the 424th?' The orderly didn't even check his stride. 'Dead.' To Quast, everything looked misty and sounded infinitely remote. Another orderly threaded his way between the rows of stretchers. 'Chest wound,' Quast called feebly. 'Operation – quick!' But all the figures that bent over him and brushed the hair off his damp forehead with the backs of their hands – figures in blood-stained aprons and shirts with rolled-up sleeves – just looked at him intently, felt his pulse, and said, 'Yes, yes,' before hurrying on. The ranks around him thinned as stretcher after stretcher was carried out. The orderlies' footsteps rang more and more hollowly.

At last it was his turn. Though hovering on the verge of unconsciousness, he felt them pick up the stretcher. Two tall doors opened to reveal a brightly lit room with a narrow white table in the centre. The black-and-white checkerboard floor was being swabbed by a man in his undershirt and braces. He was wearing a big brown rubber apron, and the water in his bucket was tinged with red. Quast closed his eyes. Operating theatre, he thought – they always clean up after every operation, well organized . . .

But then a second pair of doors swung open. They carried him into a sea of gloom. He caught sight of a Hindenburg candle perched on a bayonet stuck in the

253

wall. There was no time to see more, because the stretcher suddenly keeled over, pitching him into some straw. He tried to speak, but the doors slammed shut.

25

AUTHOR: *When a person survives a thing like that doesn't it compel him to believe in a merciful God?*
QUAST: *That's my business, but since you ask – yes, naturally it puts a different complexion on the world . . . and your own little span of existence. What I mean is, you gain a very personal relationship to – well, God, if you like. But it doesn't have anything to do with Christian self-congratulation. Just because you're granted something, there's no call to pride yourself on it. And I was granted an entire lifetime.*

Quast was shivering with cold. He felt sick and weak and unable to comprehend what had happened to him or where he was. He retched. His thoughts became muddled. Every soldier should have a cap, he told himself. He groped around in the straw. Was it there, his cap? His eyes had grown accustomed to the darkness. Although he could see, he was too weak to be frightened or shocked by what he saw. There was a man beside him with his overcoat unbuttoned and his head thrown back. He was dead. Quast was so weak he could scarcely move. Had he imagined it? No, the man was there all right: he could see his bared teeth. He wasn't thinking straight any more. He'd begun by looking for his cap, but why? Visual impressions became enmeshed with dream images. All at once, he was back in school. The surface of the bench was furrowed and pitted, adorned with ink stains and stick figures. The inkwell was empty and had a black crust around the rim. They'd been told to draw a family tree. Ah yes, there was Möller, the art teacher, in his scruffy velvet jacket – or was it old Blaschke with his gold pince-nez, or Lieutenant Ellberg and Colonel Hawk-nose come to pluck cannon fodder off his family tree? But he had to draw one first, and he couldn't if he kept his right arm raised in the Hitler salute. He lowered it. The general nodded approvingly and waved his manacled hands. Draw, Quast, draw! Female antecedents are represented by circles, male by rectangles. He tried to draw rectangles, but all he produced were circles and more circles . . .

The lofty room had whitewashed walls. At one end, just below the ceiling, was a row of small windows. Lashed by the wind, a bare branch tapped incessantly on one of the panes. Grey light slanted in and fell on the double doors at the far end, the bayonet stuck in the wall, the extinguished Hindenburg candle.

Quast opened his eyes wide. Memory flooded back. He looked to the right: sure enough, there was the dead man. He looked to the left: frozen profiles, sagging jaws, an upraised yellow hand – more corpses. Then right again: a scarecrow with blood-matted hair had propped himself on one elbow. His eyes were unseeing. 'A cup of coffee,' he gasped, 'a cup of . . .' He fell back, and the panting ceased. Quast lay quite still. His flesh crawled. Where was he? Was this what death was like, or had they forgotten him? He listened, but all he could hear was the tapping on the window-pane, now rain-streaked. He peered between his boots. More corpses, some so close to the opposite wall that their heads had been forced forward on their chests. His eyes travelled from figure to figure.

One of them winked at him. He started and looked again. Yes, it winked, opened its mouth, and said feebly, 'You alive too?' Quast whispered back, 'Yes, I think so.'

By a hairbreadth, he'd escaped being dumped into one of the mass graves that surrounded every field hospital.

They'd crossed him off their list and put him in with the dead, but Corporal Quast was still in the land of the living.

'You can operate on me right away,' he told the doctor who tried to explain why patients like him were classified as dead – why it was more important to save ten wounded men than wrestle for hours with a hopeless case. There was no point in operating, the doctor told him. The hole they'd made in him was big enough already. Why make it any bigger? His wounds were simply strapped up.

He was in luck. Somebody had just died, so he got his bed in a small ward on the first floor. On the wall, someone had scrawled, 'Iron Cross for sale. Would swap for pair of running shoes.' The other beds were occupied by silent, exhausted men. A doctor came to give Quast a shot but couldn't find the vein and probed for it painfully. Quast said, 'Isn't there anyone here who can see straight?'

The orderly standing behind the doctor said, 'Watch it, son, that's the major you're talking to.'

'And it's me he's hurting,' said Quast.

The major laughed. 'Never say die, eh?' But Quast wasn't so sure any more – he hadn't been sure of anything for a long time.

It was night again. He felt someone trying to remove his watch and jerked his wrist away. Waking in the small hours, he discovered that his feet had been stripped of the woollen socks he'd been given by a Latvian farmer's wife. You see, he told himself, that proves you're back in the land of the living.

By the afternoon of the following day, he was lying in the open on a quayside in Liepaja. He heard bombs exploding, heard two sailors sharing a cigarette beside him say that the hospital had been hit. Poor Elisabeth, he thought.

Opposite him, two Slav auxiliaries deposited a stretcher on the cobblestones. Lying on it was a bloodless figure with yellow hair and a pinched face. Quast recognized the

257

face. Once, when he'd been crouching in a foxhole, a Tiger tank had pulled up right beside him. The hatch in front of the turret opened – the one above the jutting barrel of the radio operator's machine gun – and the flaxen-headed man peered out. 'Careful you don't snap my aerial off!' Quast shouted above the roar of the engines, and the flaxen-haired man shouted back, 'I'm surprised you can hear anything at all, you mole, you!' Quast beckoned to him. 'Come down out of that sardine can and listen in!' They grinned at each other. Then came a deafening crash, and cascades of earth rained down on the Tiger's hull. The face disappeared, the hatch clanged shut, and the Tiger moved off with a screech of tracks. A moment later, it was lost to view behind some rising ground.

The flaxen-haired man smiled feebly and raised the transparent white hand that protruded from his greasy denim cuff. 'What happened to your sardine can?' Quast asked. The waxen thumb pointed skywards. 'So you'll have to learn to walk again, eh?' The other man didn't answer, just shook his head. Looking at where the bulge of his legs should have been, Quast saw a flat expanse of blanket with a haversack on top. 'Both of them?' he asked. The flaxen-haired man turned away and sighed. Then he looked at Quast and said, 'Never mind, I'll them to fix me a new pair. The old ones were knock-kneed anyway.' Two orderlies came and picked up his stretcher with effortless ease.

The coaster's hold was packed with wounded. Quast learned that the last ship to sail had struck a mine and sunk only two hours before. He took stock of his surroundings. If anything happened, the tub wouldn't last three minutes. He persuaded the orderlies to put him amidships, on the theory that the motion would be less pronounced there. He looked round for the flaxen-haired man but couldn't see him in the dim light. He pulled the blanket over his head. Not long after the vessel left harbour and began to ride the swell, the first sufferers started groaning. A sour smell filled the air.

Forty hours later, Quast was unloaded from a hospital train in Munich. They removed his lice-infested shirt with its two blood-encrusted holes, fore and aft. Then he was lifted on to a stretcher and wheeled into a basement room with tiled walls and harsh white lights overhead. Torrents of hot water descended on his naked body. An orderly gave his face a cursory wipe and asked if he had any smokes. Quast said, 'Piss off, you make me sick.' He stood up, tired of being toted around and pestered for cigarettes.

At 4 A.M., a broad-hipped, motherly-looking nurse finally showed him to his bed, a real hospital bed with adjustable sections at each end and fresh-smelling white sheets. He fell fast asleep. He slept the sleep of a drained and exhausted man whose one desire was not to surface for the next three days.

Less than an hour later, another nurse shook him by the shoulder. 'Wake up! I need your personal particulars. You'll have plenty of time to sleep later on. Come on, I can't stand here all night.'

Quast drew a deep breath. Then he let fly. He shouted that he wanted some peace at long last. He shouted his opinion of cow-faced nurses with fingers like white veal sausages who dared to lay hands on him, Herbert Quast. The nurse didn't understand. She threatened to report him to the medical superintendent. Quast shouted to her to fetch the surgeon general himself. He proposed to shove his personal particulars up the surgeon general's ass – *if* there was room for them there with the nurse already in residence. All the impotent fury within him vented itself in one long, cataclysmic outburst. His fellow patients were sitting up in bed by now. The nurse had started crying. Some orderlies came in and forced Quast's head back onto the pillows.

He was left in peace. The other occupants of the ward

avoided his eye and didn't dare speak to him. The nurses checked his temperature and pulse in silence. The man in the next bed, a middle-aged reservist who'd had an ingrowing toe-nail removed at public expense, received a visit from his wife and daughter. The three of them whispered together, looking across at Quast with a mixture of awe, revulsion, and pity.

Every morning at eleven, aircraft droned through the sky far above – long-range reconnaissance planes from U.S. bases in Italy. The bombers arrived half an hour later. Quast sat in the hospital cellar, listening to radio reports of strong enemy formations in the Munich area and reflecting that he'd never get better this way. He continued to run a temperature and found it hard to sleep at night.

Battalion had sent him an official citation: 'Promoted sergeant for gallantry in the face of the enemy.' He buttoned the pale grey braided shoulder straps to his battle-dress blouse. 'In the face of the enemy' sounded good, he thought. Where was this, Hohenfriedberg in 1745 or Munich in 1944? He recalled the sleepy, unwary young lieutenant who'd doubtless collected an Iron Cross First Class because his rear guard had fought so valiantly during the night attack on the farm. He recalled the unknown man who'd cowered among his slaughtered comrades before carrying him to safety on his back. He recalled the two privates who'd lugged him through a hail of bullets, grinding their teeth, even though they valued their own skins more than his. He recalled the sergeant who'd have driven him to hell and back because he, Quast, was a member of his own battalion. Fear and courage: two sides of the same coin. Who could lay claim to one without the other? The real bastards, he thought, burning with rage and hatred, were the home-front heroes – the ones who preached

260

about dishing it out but were too yellow to take it themselves.

It had been a long train journey to Poznań. 'You'd better stay right here for surgery,' he was told when he reported to the hospital there to have his wounds dressed. He accepted the doctor's verdict with a submissive nod. An hour later he was back in a ward. All the forty beds were occupied. He needed more surgery because his hip and thigh had still not healed after six whole months. The hospital authorities in Munich had been happy to see the last of him. 'You're right,' the medical officer had said, 'we can't do anything more for you here.' In reality, he was glad to be rid of a malcontent who scoffed at regulations and frightened the nurses.

Quast was in pain. He was also sick to death of lying there and knew he somehow had to get away, as soon as he could, from a place where everyone was sapped of strength and set on edge by the very presence of everyone else.

His next-door neighbour was a bony, taciturn private of forty-two, a farmer in civilian life. Both his feet had been blue-black with frostbite from toe to instep. Now they'd been amputated. Still anaesthetized, he tossed his head from side to side and muttered unintelligibly. All at once, he started to make sense. 'Hitler's a son of a bitch!' he yelled.

'Quick,' said Quast, 'shut the door!'

'Tell him to give me my feet back,' raved the farmer. 'I'll never drive a tractor again – I'm a cripple!'

Quast shook him. 'Keep quiet, man!'

'We all kept quiet, and now my feet are off!'

'Quiet, I said!'

'Only when I get my feet back from that bastard Hitler!'

Quast hoped no Nazi devotee had heard. 'The man's delirious,' he explained to the ward at large, ' – he doesn't know what he's saying. You didn't hear a word, understand?'

The others nodded. The farmer came round slowly. He moaned all night. Quast filled his tumbler, straightened his pillows, tried to console him with talk of miraculous artificial limbs, pointed out that he could stay at home on his farm from now on. The farmer's response was scornful.

'You Hitler Youth fanatics! It was youngsters like you made this war.'

So turning your back on the past was as easy as that, thought Quast. Not only had the farmer developed a bad memory; he'd already found a convenient scapegoat. He wondered when the man had first voted for Hitler. Thirty-three? He might even have been a mounted stormtrooper or head of the local branch of the Party's agricultural association.

Christmas Eve 1944. Loopholes were being knocked in the hospital's outside walls. Quast heard this from Manes, the Rhinelander who occupied the bed opposite his and was already allowed to walk. They eyed each other in silence. At length, Quast said, 'They're for the flagpoles, when we celebrate final victory.'

That afternoon, they stuffed a pair of blue striped hospital pyjamas with pillows, added some boots, and laid the dummy out on Kalle's bed. Kalle himself hid behind the door. Then they called Nurse Tula, a shortsighted, heavy-footed woman in her sixties. She saw the figure on the bed, gasped, and waddled resolutely over to the supposed miscreant. 'This is the limit! You naughty boy – with your boots on, too!' When she reached out to haul Kalle of the bed, he fell to pieces – a gruesome travesty of what was happening all over Europe. For an instant, Tula froze. Then she turned, surveyed the rows of beds with menace, and suddenly grinned from ear to ear. 'What babies you are! Hardly able to crawl, but you're always up to some kind of mischief.' She was still laughing in the passage outside. 'Those boys,' they heard her saying, 'those boys!' It sounded a little bit wistful.

In the evening, the big table in the centre of the ward was decked with sprigs of fir and lighted candles. The general arrived, a portly gentleman whose belt traversed his paunch like a barrel hoop. Though well meant, his Christmas address failed to strike the right note. When the words 'final victory' rang out, Manes suddenly went into convulsions and moaned, 'My head, my head!' The general was taken aback. 'A serious case, General,' said Tula, who realized that her 'boys' wanted to get rid of him. 'Better not go on. They're all in a critical condition.' The MO in attendance gave a puzzled frown. He knew better, but before he could intervene the general broke off. 'Next ward,' he murmured, and went. Perhaps he was relieved at not having to say any more. Tula waddled after him. At the door, she turned and wagged a wrinkled forefinger, but her false teeth flashed in another broad grin.

Quast was still awake at two o'clock next morning, thanks to the pain in his hip. He lay there staring at the ceiling. Beside him, Kalle lit a cigarette and noticed that his eyes were open. He extinguished the match with a jet of tobacco smoke.

'That general,' he said. 'When you come down to it, he's just another poor clod like you or me.'

'Sure,' muttered Quast, 'except that he's lived longer.'

Anna was on night duty. Mid twenties, medium height, ripe lips, rounded hips, shapely legs. Four tough years of nursing had given her face a tart expression, but her dark eyes glowed and her voice acquired a strange timbre whenever she saw Quast, who found her equally attractive. After finishing her pill-and-injection round, she turned in the doorway and cocked an eyebrow at him. Then she disappeared, the crossed straps of her apron looking almost fluorescent in the bluish emergency lighting.

Midnight came. Quast got quietly out of bed, slipped into his hospital bathrobe, and hobbled out. He could walk again. Gone at last were the days when thirty-nine men had shared in his digestive processes, just as he had in theirs. Standing on his own two legs was the key to a modicum of independence. Weak as he was, he rejoiced in his new mobility.

But he wasn't thinking of that now. Outside in the corridor, Anna rustled past him with a kidney-shaped pan containing swabs and a hypo. 'The linen room,' she whispered. 'See you in five minutes.' He knew where she meant. There was a little cubbyhole next door with a couch inside.

He shuffled along, feeling like a candidate for the stiffest of examinations. For weeks now, ever since his last operation, he'd been plagued by the thought that he mightn't be a man any more – that he wouldn't be any use to a woman. Would his worst fears be confirmed, or had he been tormenting himself for no good reason?

He was sitting on the couch with his head hanging and a woebegone expression on his face, sick with nerves, when Anna appeared. There was nothing apprehensive about the light in her eyes and the purr in her throat as she purposefully stripped off anything that might impede their movements.

Anna was an elemental force. She wouldn't listen when he tried to broach his problem – she thought he was embarrassed by his scars, hampered by his bandages, or simply shy. She engulfed him like a mountain torrent and swept him along with her. Unable to dwell on his misgivings any longer, he was overjoyed to find them unfounded. Anna remedied any deficiencies on his part with wholehearted ingenuity, transmuting his clumsiness into artistic refinements that left him dazed with delight. She sobbed as the tension drained out of her, then lay beside him, moist-eyed. It was only when she hurriedly re-arranged her clothing that he noticed the ladies' automatic.

'What's that for?'

'Five for the Ivans, one for me.'

'But we're bound to get away.'

'You, yes. I don't have any illusions about my own chances. I'm from Volhynia. The Reds locked me up one time – only for a week, but that was enough. No more prison cells and interrogation rooms for me. Reds or Brownshirts, they're all the same.'

'You honestly mean you'd – '

'Why not? I've never gone to bed with a man I didn't like, and I don't intend to change my ways because of the Russians. There's not much to choose between being liberated by them and the Germans – you know that as well as I do. Besides, they've got attractive ways of converting women to Communism. I'd sooner call it quits.'

'But Anna, why don't you simply leave now, while there's still time?'

'Don't you like the service here?' She smiled indulgently, tying her apron. 'I've lived an honest life and I want to die an honest death, if you know what I mean. Of course, I could have imagined something better for myself – a decent man, say, and a couple of kids. Not just shutting dead men's eyes the whole time, or coping with pus and shit and swapping badinage with cripples who still haven't grasped what poor fish they'll be without their uniforms and medals – not being a good Samaritan, just a woman . . . We're living in a great age, though, and it's too damned great for me.'

He stared at her in consternation, but she laughed and ruffled his hair. 'You'd better go now, sweetheart,' she said. Then she drew his face up to hers and kissed him. Five minutes later he was back in bed, tired and contented but stricken by what she had told him.

* * *

265

Like the other occupants of the truck, he had been issued a pillow for delivery to the next hospital that admitted them. The streets were deserted, though shots could be heard in the distance. Polish partisans were all they needed, he thought, but they reached the freight train unscathed.

The boxcar's floorboards were carpeted with filthy straw. '8 Horses or 30 Men', he read as they climbed aboard. He flopped down and stared out into the drizzle. The locomotive gave a screech, and clouds of white steam spurted from its piston valves. Outside, more trucks pulled up with a squeal of brakes, and shouted orders rent the air: the next trainload had started to assemble. The boxcar gave a jerk. Couplings clanked as they took the strain. A cigarette butt landed on the ballast and lay there glowing faintly.

Quast chugged westwards as he had once done eastwards, penned up in a draughty boxcar with a piece of cookhouse bread in his pocket.

26

AUTHOR: *Were you entitled to disband the men like that?*

QUAST: *I was in command.*

AUTHOR: *Yes, but they were meant to be a combat unit.*

QUAST: *So?*

AUTHOR: *So you could have fought till you were captured.*

QUAST: *We'd had enough of being pushed around. Better hungry on the outside than well fed behind barbed wire – at least, that was the original idea.*

For a while yet, Quast was shuttled to and fro amid the ruins of the Third Reich, that political edifice whose would-be grandeur was now being destroyed by its own excesses and the homicidal mania of the man who had built it.

Then he was ordered to lead a makeshift infantry platoon against the Americans. He studied the map, listened to the all-encompassing thunder of artillery fire, and surveyed the sullen faces of his thirty new charges. They were a motley collection: anti-aircraft gunners who'd blown up their guns, bailed-out tank crewmen, toil-worn engineers, harassed infantrymen. One of the latter wore a silver-braided sniper's badge on his right forearm, signifying that he had at least forty kills to his credit.

'Still got your gun?' Quast asked him.

The sniper, a ginger-haired corporal named Jan, shrugged. 'Sure, but what's the point?'

If he wasn't careful, thought Quast, he'd have them all on his conscience: the young ones who still didn't know the score, and the old ones who knew it all too well but couldn't see any way out. What had the general told him that time in the farmhouse beside Lake Ladoga? *Courage is a fine thing, but remember: courage plus conscience is worth even more . . .*

He'd been given his orders in the playground of a village school, alias company headquarters. 'Reconnoitre in the direction of Megerbach,' he was told. 'And take some prisoners. The Yanks are easy meat. Most of them are scared shitless.' And no wonder, he thought, when they'd already won the war.

He led his men to the edge of a forest track that converged with the road to Megerbach. The little strip of asphalt toiled bravely uphill and down before descending into the rain-washed valley where the village lay.

'If you want to be around for the victory celebrations,' said Quast, 'keep off the track and under cover.' They all flopped down in the bracken, hungry and battle-weary. Quast beckoned to Jan. 'Corporal, you come with me.' The sniper nodded. He didn't speak until they'd trudged through the wood for several minutes. Then he said, 'Look, Sergeant, you aren't really going to do what that twerp told you, are you?' He meant the lieutenant who'd sent them out on patrol. Quast shrugged. 'No reason why we shouldn't take a peek.'

They looked down into the valley. The village was teeming with khaki-clad figures. Parked in every open space were tanks, trucks, and jeeps with bright red air identification symbols painted on their turrets and hoods. Taking advantage of a convenient hedge, they slunk down to the rear of the nearest house, which was built into the hillside. One bound, and they were outside the back door. Two steps, and they were in the low-ceilinged farmhouse kitchen. Seated at the table were an old woman with stringy white hair, a girl in a kerchief and flowered apron, and two middle-aged men. One of the small windows, which looked out on a yard, was obscured by the side of an olive-drab army truck. The gargling sounds that drifted in bore little resemblance to the English Quast had learned in school. On the table stood a load of snow-white bread, partly sliced, a can of bacon, a can of peanut butter, and a carton of Camels.

The men and the girl jumped up in alarm; the old woman sat there blinking. They all put their hands up. The younger of the two farmers turned pale and started shaking. Quast wondered if his army uniform was wrapped round a brick under six feet of liquid manure.

'What's the matter,' he said, charitably ignoring the younger man,' – forgotten what a German looks like?'

They slowly lowered their arms. The older man said, 'For God's sake, there are Americans outside. Are you Werewolves? Don't shoot!'

'Stop blathering,' Quast told him. 'How long have they been there? How many are there? What's the name of their outfit? Quick!'

'Criminals,' mumbled the old woman. 'Nazi swine! There's been enough killing.'

Quast could hardly believe his ears. 'So that's how it is,' said Jan. He appropriated a pack of Camels and stuffed some white bread into his mouth. The men told them when the Americans had arrived and roughly how many there were, the girl pushed the bread and bacon towards them, the old woman snarled at them. All four could hardly wait to see the last of them. When they were safely back in the wood and grinning at each other, Quast said, 'Now we'll send a runner to the lieutenant. I know it's pointless, but it'll make him feel good.'

They were hardly back with the men, who had drifted into the clearing and were standing around shivering, when they heard the drone of an American spotter plane. 'Into the trees,' Quast yelled, 'and don't anyone move!'

The high-wing monoplane skimmed the treetops, banking gently. From under his helmet rim, Quast could clearly see the observer scanning the ground through big horn-rimmed glasses. The roar of the engine receded. 'Anyone know what it's like, being shelled in a wood!' A few of the men nodded. Most of them stared at Quast with furrowed brows. 'It's no fun, believe me. The things burst in the branches and the whole shower of shit comes down on top of you. You can hug the ground as much as you like, but it doesn't help. So remember, next time don't move a muscle.'

The spotter plane made another circuit. The men tucked their heads in and didn't budge until it had swooped into the valley and out of sight. Then they all straightened up and stared at each other. 'Listen,' said Quast. 'Do exactly as I say. No shooting, do you hear? If the Yanks come this way, let them through, understand?' The men looked and sounded relieved.

Quast sighted a few stray members of his platoon on the other side of the track and sprinted across to have a word with them. As he did so, he saw the snout of a tank gun come nosing over the brow of the hill, heard the familiar roar of engines and the hateful metallic jingle of caterpillar tracks. He reached the trees just as the tank's hull breasted the rise and the barrel swung down at the clearing. 'No shooting!' he shouted again, burrowing deep into the brushwood and brambles. The steel colossus lumbered past. Then came some olive-drab infantrymen with short-barrelled rifles. They looked around warily but didn't venture into the trees. Bringing up the rear were several jeeps with machine-gun mountings. The leading vehicle halted and the crew got out. One GI strolled over to the edge of the wood with a roll of khaki-coloured toilet paper in his hand and dropped his pants within feet of Quast's lair. Another came and squatted nearby. Quast's first close contact with the US Army was a worm's eye view of two backsides. Better than an eyeball-to-eyeball encounter with the Russians, he reflected.

The column moved on. Silence fell at last. Quast crept out of the undergrowth and straightened up. When he called his men together, there were only eighteen left. The rest had turned free-lance, some hoping to reach home under their own steam, others preferring to give themselves up.

Quast said, 'All right, gentlemen, mission accomplished. We're now behind the American lines. Anyone feel like playing partisan?' Their narrowed eyes conveyed an unspoken question: Had their sergeant lost his marbles? 'Very well,' he said. 'We don't have any arms and ammunition to speak of, we don't have any orders, and we aren't in the mood any more. Good. I hereby release you from your oath of allegiance. Go home – dismiss, fall out, so long, kiss my ass. Take your pick.'

They straggled off, relieved but unsure of themselves – relieved at not being called on to fight but unsure because now, after all these years, they were no longer bound by orders and dependent on higher authority.

Eight men lingered in a group around Quast. Jan said, 'Sergeant, that was pretty good thinking. You've got a map, haven't you, and your home's up north. Well, we want to go home too. How about taking us along?'

Quast tried to analyse their expressions. Some of them, he guessed, preferred to tag along because the sight of a sergeant's shoulder straps still gave them confidence, others because they'd taken a shine to him or thought they might have fared worse without him. 'All right,' he said, 'but we'll hang on to our rifles. We don't seem to have many friends left in Germany. Let's go.'

They tramped the Westphalian highlands for a week. American troops controlled nearly all the roads and most of the villages, though German stragglers roamed the forests and regular German units fiercely defended their few remaining strongholds. Quast and his party steered clear of everyone and everything. It rained incessantly. Their boots sank deep into the waterlogged ground and became waterlogged themselves. One night, they bivouacked in some undergrowth above an American battery that fired over their heads at regular intervals. Sleep was impossible. When dawn came, two of their number were missing – two older men who'd become progressively more sullen and silent as the days went by.

'Hey, is the war over yet?' The voice came from a raised blind screened by dense foliage. A solitary soldier's quizzical face peered down through the greenery.

'Not yet,' Jan called back. 'What are you doing up there?'

'Waiting for the shit to stop flying. I've got enough food and drink to last me for the duration, so I've pulled up the ladder. If you can think of a better idea, tell me.'

An artist in survival, thought Quast, waiting in his own eccentric way for peace to descend. 'All the best,' he called. 'See you after the war.'

They came to a forest track flanked by American field-telephone cables. Vehicles could be heard approaching from both directions. First on the scene was an SPW, or German armoured troop carrier. Just as it crawled into view, a US Medical Corps convoy appeared. The foremost jeep, which was flying a Red Cross flag, ended up nose to nose with the SPW. In the SPW stood a grinning, bullet-headed German sergeant; in the jeep, holding onto the windshield, a gaunt US medical officer with gold-rimmed glasses.

'I'm taking you prisoner,' said the sergeant.

The doctor shook his head. 'Oh no you don't. Your war's over. Anyway, we're medical personnel. Better come along with us.'

'The hell with that,' said the sergeant. 'No PW camp for me.' He brought the muzzle of his MG42 to bear on the leading jeep.

'Germany's *kaputt*,' the doctor said. 'Come down out of there.'

Quast turned to Jan. 'Quick,' he said in a low voice, 'get round behind that madman and drop him if he opens up

272

on the medics.' He signalled to the others to take cover on the edge of the trees. Then he darted out between the two warring parties with his rifle at the hip.

'Great,' said the sergeant. 'Welcome aboard, friend.'

The doctor looked dismayed. 'Geneva Convention,' he said. '*Nix mehr* fighting.'

Quast addressed himself to the bullet-headed sergeant. 'If you pull that trigger, you're dead. There's a sniper behind you.' The sergeant looked round. His eyes widened and he let go of the machine gun. 'Where are you heading?' asked Quast.

'Home, of course.'

'Fine, your wife'll be pleased.' Quast turned and called into the trees. 'Let the crate through!' Five rifle muzzles dipped in acknowledgement. 'All right,' said Quast, 'get going, but make it snappy.'

The sergeant relapsed into the driving seat, looking bemused, and slammed the SPW into gear. Quast motioned to the doctor. 'Get those jeeps out of the way.' The American drivers hurriedly pulled off the track. At that moment, Quast caught sight of six men on the edge of the wood: camouflage jackets, open collars, black gorgets with white runes, steel helmets with camouflage covers. Play it cool, he told himself. He waved as the bullet-headed sergeant trundled past in his steel coffin, grinning once more. Ignoring the Waffen SS men, he went over to the US medical officer, who had suddenly turned pale. One of the men in camouflage jackets materialized beside him. His head was bandaged. Out of the corner of his eye, Quast noted the single star that marked him as an SS sergeant. Not an officer – so much the better.

'What's going on here?' said the SS man.

Quast didn't look round. 'Where to?' he asked the doctor.

'We're going to pick up some casualties.' The American pointed up the track. Gunfire could be heard in the distance.

'You look after German soldiers too?'

'Naturally. Doctors look after everyone – the Hippocratic oath, you know. I studied at Göttingen.'

'Mind if I check that out with your men?'

'Sure, ask any of them.'

Quast didn't bother. He raised his voice. 'This medical team is going up front. It looks after our boys as well as theirs. Hands off the medics, understand?'

'Yes, Sergeant,' came a ragged chorus from his own five men in the bushes.

'Stop,' said the SS sergeant; 'not so fast.'

Quast waved the doctor on. 'Get out of here, quick!'

The doctor turned and beckoned to his men. 'Drive on!' he shouted. The jeeps got under way. Their apprehensive occupants relaxed as the truth sank in. They threw cigarettes and chewing gum to the men in the undergrowth, laughing and whistling. A black corpsman tossed a carton of K rations on to the track. The doctor raised his hand in salute.

'You've got brains,' he called. 'The war's as good as over. Why not come too?'

Quast shook his head. 'Thank you, but no. We don't like barbed wire.'

The doctor shrugged. The convoy ground past, wreathing the trees in exhaust fumes. All that broke the ensuing silence was a patter of rain and the gunfire that rolled around the mountains like distant thunder.

The SS sergeant glared at Quast. 'What the hell?' he snapped. 'We could have commandeered those jeeps.'

'What about the rules of war? Don't you subscribe to them in the Waffen SS? Listen, if you stopped a bullet, you'd be damned glad of a shot in the arm from anyone, Yank or no Yank. Well, wouldn't you?'

The SS sergeant chewed his lip and nodded, half convinced.

'I didn't stay stand down!' Quast shouted to his men. 'Stay in the trees. Everything under control, Jan?'

'Sure,' Jan shouted back. 'Just let him try something, that's all!'

'What's that supposed to mean?' demanded the SS sergeant.

Quast parried the question with another. 'Where are you from?'

'We're all that's left of an NCO training school. The rest are dead. We don't know where to head for. Come on, comrade, let's team up.'

Quast looked at his twitching face, then at the other SS men standing helplessly in the undergrowth with their arms limp and their weapons lowered, not daring to move. Toothless lions, he thought – at the end of their rope, poor bastards. 'All right,' he called to his party, 'you can come out now.' They all assembled on the track, SS men included. 'We don't want to team up – we've got plans of our own. Besides, there'd be too many of us for safety.'

The SS sergeant sighed. 'Maybe you're right.'

'We'll divide the food, then we'll make ourselves scarce. Better not save any American stuff for later. If they catch us, they may get the wrong idea. All kinds of dirty work could be going on in these woods.'

'Fair enough,' said the SS sergeant.

They all munched and smoked as if their lives depended on it. Quast told them to bury the empty cans and wrappers. Then they plodded off, leaving the six dejected SS men sitting beside the track.

Four days later they came to an isolated house. After keeping it under observation for some time, they cautiously approached it. A thin thread of smoke was curling from the chimney. They were soaked to the skin and shivering with cold and hunger. Nobody came when they knocked, so they hammered on the door with their rifle butts. Finally it opened. A woman of about fifty stood there with her arms akimbo.

'Go away at once!' she snapped. 'The Americans may

get here any minute, and Dictor Pingel doesn't want to be disturbed until they do. Besides, just look at you!'

Quast saw red. He jabbed his gun muzzle into the woman's apron, somewhere near her navel. 'All right, now run off and tell your boss we're going to have a warm-up in his front parlour, whether he's at home to us or not. And take a look in the larder. Bread and butter'll do. You can save your champagne for the Yanks.'

The woman gasped. The soldiers laughed, but not pleasantly.

Ponderous furniture à la Reich Chancellery, ankle-deep carpets, engravings on the walls, silver chandeliers – Herr Pingel had turned his hunting lodge into a luxurious retreat. He didn't show his face. They changed their steaming socks and stripped off their sodden underwear. Jan said, 'If that old bitch doesn't come back, I'll shoot Pingel's lights off the ceiling.' But come back she did. Ungraciously, she plunked a loaf of bread and a can of butter on the table – on a silver tray. 'Please don't put yourself out,' Quast told her. They sliced the bread and spread it with half an inch of butter, then wolfed it with their rifles resting on the sumptuous carpets and their muddy boots parked beneath the gleaming table. Herr Pingel's housekeeper hovered in the doorway, eyeing them distastefully.

'So,' said Quast, when they were ready to move on, 'give the director our regards and thank him for his generous hospitality. Tell him Heil Hitler from us – he's bound to remember the phrase.'

27

AUTHOR: *Have you put it all behind you now?*
QUAST: *I can't.*
AUTHOR: *You mean you feel sorry for yourself?*
QUAST: *I don't take myself that seriously.*
AUTHOR: *But there aren't many laughs in your story.*
QUAST: *There wasn't much to laugh at.*

Four days later they were captured. They failed to spot some Americans sneaking up behind them while they crouched in the grass beside a highway, waiting to scoot across as soon as a gap appeared in the columns of trucks and tanks that were streaming past in the dusk. They threw their rifles away. The Americans were rough with them but not brutal. Quast was amazed how fluent his English became with a gun against the small of his back – the words simply popped into his head like magic. One of the GIs removed his cheap army wristwatch. Prompted by a belief in the universality of American wealth and devotion to justice, he complained to a young lieutenant.

'Geneva Convention?' he said tentatively.

'Sure, we know. Your watch has been confiscated, that's all.'

'*Quittung?*' said Quast. 'Er, receipt?'

'Later,' said the lieutenant.

Next morning they were driven to some kind of head-quarters. As senior NCO, Quast was separated from the others and taken for interrogation. A red-faced lieuten-ant was seated at a table on the edge of a farmyard. Flanking him were two bespectacled GIs who spoke

German with a Berlin accent. One of them reminded Quast of Itzi Warschauer, the Jewish schoolmate who'd emigrated in their third year at Charlottenburg Primary. He was halted five yards short of the table and told to wait. The sergeant being questioned before him seemed intent on having an argument. 'Name, rank, and number,' he said, 'that's all you'll get out of me.' The lieutenant growled something, but the sergeant firmly shook his head. The lieutenant made a curt gesture. One of the Berlin GIs kicked the refractory sergeant in the back of the knees. As he started to go down, the other punched him in the kidneys. With a groan, he collapsed in the mud and lay there squirming. Two more GIs hurried forward and dragged him behind a barn.

The lieutenant said, 'Next!' If he wanted a story, thought Quast, he could have one. There was no point in keeping quiet about his unit and its original mission, but the lieutenant showed little interest.

'Any more of your guys up there?' He pointed at the blue-black mountains under their mantle of rain.

'Plenty,' said Quast. 'Two companies of Waffen SS, pretty fresh. Three Panthers, brand-new. One radio truck, damaged.'

'What!' said the lieutenant. He jumped up and pushed a map across the table. 'Where, exactly?'

Quast looked at the map. He'd actually seen the tanks abandoned in a clearing and the radio truck nearby with all its equipment destroyed. He indicated a spot miles away from where he'd last seen the half dozen desperate SS men and the sergeant in the SPW. The lieutenant transferred his gum to the other cheek and shouted something. Troops poured out of the barn, jeep and half-track engines roared into life. The lieutenant ran to a scout car with long radio aerials. Quast had ceased to be an object of interest. A GI emerged from behind the barn and jerked a thumb over his shoulder. 'Come on, you fucking Nazi,' he said.

Hustled through a wire-mesh gate, Quash found himself standing, up to his ankles in mire, with a hundred other prisoners. He was inside a cage – the first of many. Jan waded over and slapped him on the back.

They were loaded into trucks. At midnight, Quast read the familiar legend on a line of boxcars: '8 Horses or 30 Men.' An hour later they were on their way to France.

Quast read of German atrocities and cold-blooded sadism. He saw press photographs of those who had humiliated and exterminated defenceless millions in the name of Hitler's cause, and their faces stirred uneasy memories of the Schapers and Herbsts, the Ellbergs and Schacks, the Briegels and Behnkes. He was persistently addressed as 'fucking Nazi'. He read what was understood by the term Nazi and resented its application to himself. He heard the expression 'collective guilt' and guessed how quick the sadists of the Brownshirt era would be to shelter beneath its umbrella, rubbing their hands at such a convenient dilution of responsibility. He was doubled around in grey denims with the letters 'PW' on his back and told that the uniform he'd worn for years was a murderer's get-up – when all it had been, in his opinion, was uncomfortable and unpractical. So all murderers could be identified by their field-grey uniforms: was it really that simple?

He was astonished to hear that the Allies planned to do away with Prussia. He pondered the question in his tent at night, rolled up in a blanket on two thicknesses of cardboard, while sentries patrolled the nearby fence with a rhythmical creak of boot leather. Do away with Prussia? He could imagine them doing away with Prussian bureaucracy and red tape, but the Prussia he'd believed in had nothing to do with that. Was it right to abolish something just because a few deranged individuals had made it a gruesome caricature in the eyes of the world?

One morning, when the prisoners were being assigned

fatigues by their senior NCO, a veteran sergeant major, Quast peered over his shoulder. '20 Men to 94th Signals Mess,' he read. 'Signals,' he said quickly. 'Let me handle that – I was a signaller.' And he snatched the requisition slip away before the sergeant major had time to digest its contents. He didn't mention the word 'mess.'

He selected his detail with care. Most of them were youngsters, restless and snappish as puppies, with a leavening of staid and stolid noncoms. He didn't tell them they'd been picked for cookhouse duty, that most enviable of fatigues, till the truck had lumbered out of camp.

'We'll all eat like fighting cocks if you pull your weight,' he said. 'The Yanks may be doing away with Prussia, but nothing impresses them more than Prussian spit-and-polish. So remember: plenty of heel-clicking!'

The truck pulled up and a sentry lowered the tailgate. They piled out on to a cinder-surfaced barrack square. The cookhouse, a turn-of-the-century building in institutional brickwork, was fifty yards away.

Out the door waddled a big fat sergeant with crinkly black hair, amiable Italian eyes, and a grin surmounting his numerous chins. Quast got his squad fallen in. 'Now,' he hissed, 'do your stuff.' They dressed off by the right with geometrical precision.

The sergeant put his hands on his hips and stared. Quast ordered his men to number off. Their voices rent the air, crisp as pistol shots. Disguising his limp, Quast marched up to the sergeant, who still looked slightly bewildered.

'Cookhouse squad reporting for duty. Squad commander and twenty men present, correct, and ready for inspection – sir!'

A grunt escaped the portly sergeant's breast. He ambled over to the line of poker-backed prisoners and surveyed them with benign appreciation. 'Great, just great!' he said admiringly; then, 'Morning, boys!' Quast, who was standing just behind the fat man, brought his choir in on cue. 'Morning, sir!' they bellowed in unison. Scattered applause came from a handful of watching GIs.

Quast informed the sergeant that his men were hungry and invited him to say what items of food were taboo.

'Oh, sure. No oranges, no bananas.'

'You heard the sergeant,' said Quast. 'Anyone who makes a pig of himself gets fired, understand?'

They didn't let him down. Before long, everything in the cookhouse shone like silver. The American cookhouse personnel watched their robot-like exertions appraisingly. Then one of them lit a cigarette and perched it on the edge of a table. 'Clean that up,' he said. Ingenuity had triumphed over the official ban on fraternization . . .

That evening, Quast was admitted to the camp hospital with a badly inflamed hip. After X-raying and examining him for nearly an hour, the doctors decided against further surgery. A week later, he was on his way back to Germany.

The consignment of prisoners was eighty-one strong, the eight-first being Quast. Two huge trucks swept in through the hospital gates. Eighty men and one armed guard – the regulation number – squeezed into the first of them. The driver secured the tailgate and marched back to his cab. Quast watched him go, reflecting that military minds work the same the world over. Then another guard appeared. He nudged Quast in the ribs and pointed to the second truck, grinning broadly. Quast tossed his belongings inside and scrambled up after them. The guard sat down beside him. The gum-chewing driver slammed the tailgate shut and sauntered to his cab. With a mighty roar, the truck moved off. All by themselves in the cavernous load space, Quast and his escort lolled on a bench and whistled companionably.

They drove through Paris on a balmy summer evening. Lights twinkled in many of the windows, all of which were open. Couples stood or strolled, closely entwined, on the banks of the Seine and under its numerous bridges. The combination was invariable: men in khaki, girls in colourful cotton prints. Searchlights illuminated the silver shape of a Flying Fortress on display beneath the Eiffel Tower. Tricolour flags billowed beside the Stars and Stripes, loudspeakers blared. The sidewalk cafés were thronged with laughing, animated figures. The truck, adorned with big white US stars, rolled by, exhaust throbbing, tyres drumming on the cobbles. PW Herbert Quast waved graciously to the crowds below and joined in their laughter. If he hadn't known it before, he knew it then: peace was preferable to war.

Germany again. Quast and several hundred other prisoners were in Cage 6. The huge airfield had been divided into pens like a cattle market. Wrecked German fighters littered the perimeter, and the roofs of the local town could just be seen beyond the trees. On the southern horizon, white-capped Alpine peaks jutted into a glassy summer sky.

The gate to Cage 7 was open. The American guards posted on either side of it were chewing gum with the sleepy monotony of oxen grazing a meadow.

Two by two, the prisoners had to strip to the waist and double through the gate with their hands up. This exposed the underside of their upper arms, where every member of the outlawed SS had his blood group tattooed. The Americans were conducting a final check.

Quast stood in line, idly watching the guards at work and wondering how long it would be before his turn came. A pale, tense face caught his eye. Just as he recognized its owner as the SS sergeant he'd met in the forest, the man saw him and came over.

'You've got to help me,' he whispered.

'Get this straight,' Quast retorted in a low voice. 'If you're one of the bunch who took it out on Jews and PWs, I'll turn you in myself. Better talk fast; you don't have much time.'

'Look,' said the man, 'there must have been at least a million men in the Waffen SS, and less than 5 per cent served in concentration camps and Jew-hunting outfits.'

Quast shrugged. 'Even that was 5 per cent too many.'

'I know. We often discussed it among ourselves, but I was a straightforward infantryman. I was in the Luftwaffe till last year – air gunner and radio operator. Then Göring disbanded our wing and turned us into soldiers. They sent me up front before I knew where I was. Then they told me I was wearing the wrong uniform and gave me a new one with black collar patches – just like that. I made out all right in the infantry, which was why they sent me to NCO school. Now I'm here.'

Quast chewed his lower lip. Before he could speak, the other man went on quickly. 'Listen,' he said, 'it's time people stopped tarring everyone with the same brush. First the Jews and the Slavs, now the Nazis and the SS. You really want to keep it up?'

'Never mind what I want. We're talking about you, you idiot!' Quast wondered why he felt so incensed. Because he'd been drafted into the role of judge and jury? Because of the risk he was being asked to run? Or because he'd caught himself imposing a terrible burden of guilt on someone who happened to have his blood group tattooed in blue on his arm?

The other man caught him by the elbow. 'All I meant was, you're too smart to want the same old game to go on.'

Quast jerked his arm away. 'Why pick on me?'

'I haven't had a good night's sleep for weeks – in fact I haven't slept at all since they brought us here for screening. It's been preying on my mind. I thought you'd understand, somehow.'

Quast stared at the ground and said nothing.

The other man's voice became husky. 'I'm scared, if you want to know. The Yanks have got sadists of their own – they enjoy hurting people the same as ours do. I swear I kept my nose clean. After all, I wouldn't have been running around that forest in uniform if I'd had something to hide. I'd have shot the nearest farmer and stolen his clothes.'

The young PW was desperate. Quast looked at him closely, wishing that a face could tell more about its owner's character. All he saw was a frightened young man with a lopsided bandage on his head, breathing fast and shuffling from foot to foot. As for himself, he didn't feel qualified to play the policeman or avenging angel. 'All right,' he said with a sigh, 'I'll do my best. What's your name?'

'Karl Thormann.'

Quast stationed himself beside a bulky prisoner with Thormann just to his rear. The pair in front had already passed the checkpoint. 'Next two!' Quast's partner broke into a trot. At that moment, Quast dropped his shirt. *'Mak snell, mak snell!'* shouted the guard, brandishing his rifle. Laboriously, Quast retrieved his shirt. 'Now!' he hissed, and set off. This threw the system into predictable confusion. Quast's partner was four paces ahead of him, Thormann half a pace behind.

'Move, you fucking Nazi!'

Quast and Thormann sprinted, glued together like Siamese twins. They whipped up their arms just before reaching the guard and panted, 'Sorry, sir!' The guard lunged at Quast with his rifle butt, only to be distracted by the next pair of prisoners, who had been taken by surprise and were wavering. The guard ejected his gum and beckoned them angrily. With several hundred prisoners still to check, he was disinclined to spend the entire day staring into Nazi armpits.

Thormann got through undetected. Flushed with excitement, he gave Quast's hand a surreptitious shake. An hour later they were both classified unfit for work because of their wounds and transferred to the British Zone.

* * *

The night was cold enough to make them shiver. Several of the prisoners in their new cage lay sprawled on the trampled turf, utterly exhausted. Quast and Karl, who couldn't sleep, were sitting on an upturned horse trough. Though pleased by the imminent prospect of release after months behind barbed wire, they wondered if the Allied authorities mightn't, after all, send them off to do forced labour like the able-bodied prisoners from the camp in the Alpine foothills, who'd been herded into boxcars for transportation to the coal mines of France.

They turned their thoughts to the future, though with little relish. The towns they'd passed through were ruins haunted by wan and ragged figures. Rumours had reached them of the Morgenthau Plan, under which German industry was to be dismantled and the entire country transformed into an agricultural zone. Even if it were never put into effect, how long would it take to rebuild all the devastated towns, blown bridges, and damaged highways – how long to rehouse all the countless people now roaming Germany with bundles, suitcases, and handcarts?

After a youth spent in uniform, they would now, for the very first time, be private citizens. They alternately made plans and relapsed into pensive, shivering silence. 'How about emigrating?' suggested Karl. Silence fell again, broken only by an occasional footfall as one of the others plodded past, but they both reached the same, unspoken conclusion. Now that their country was in such a pitiable state, they couldn't bring themselves to abandon it.

'It was different after 1918,' Quast said. 'People could still talk of a lost generation in those days, but now? They won't even let us lick our wounds, that's for sure.' He prodded the dew-sodden turf with the toe of his boot. 'We'll have to clear up the mess, you bet, while other people talk big and grow fat. You know the ones I mean. There are plenty of little Hitlers still around.'

Karl nodded. 'Don't remind me of that name. Know what it said on my SS belt buckle? "Mine honour is loyalty." And what did *he* do? Ran out on us – shot himself. No question of fighting to the last, the way he asked us to.'

'Of course not.' Quast grinned malignly. 'That's because we proved unworthy of him. The German people didn't deserve to survive – he said so himself before he died.' He yawned at Karl and Karl yawned back. Their faith in the Führer's pronouncements was finally extinct.

Next morning, they were crammed into a British three-tonner. Three hours later the truck pulled up outside Hamburg's Dammtor Station. A Tommy dropped the tailgate and bellowed the last military order they would ever receive.

'*Raus!* Come on, get out! Move it!'

They jumped down on to the pockmarked asphalt and stared up at the wrought-iron trelliswork of the ruined concourse. Not a scrap of glass could be seen, and the masonry had been ravaged by fire and bomb splinters. The truck drove off. While the group was dispersing, Karl shook Quast's hand. 'Well,' he said, 'I'm going to try and head north. Thanks for everything.'

'Quast grinned. '*Auf Wiedersehen*, Herr Thormann.'

'And the same to you, Herr Quast.'

Still chuckling, they went their separate ways. An odd sensation possessed them – a blend of hope and desolation, curiosity and mistrust. Mistrust above all. They were wary of being duped yet again.

Quast walked a few steps, then paused. He sat down on his bundle and surveyed the ruins around him. A long-forgotten verse from the Bible ran through his head: 'He sitteth alone and keepeth silence, because he hath borne it upon him. He putteth his mouth in the dust; if so there may be hope.'

He felt bemused, but not by the sultry midday heat. A medley of voices came crowding in, some imperious, some frightened, some imploring.

For inspection, ports arms! Yes, Sergeant! Stretcher-

bearer! The salute consists in raising the right hand smartly to the cap or helmet. The second is delivered when the first has been completed. Yes, Major! Machine-gun nest five degrees right of bushy-topped tree. Tank dead ahead! Medic! The CO's been hit! Fire at will! Yes, Lieutenant! Kettledrum calling Beehive. Changing position now, out. Medic! Fire over open sights! Ration carriers, fall out! Right away, Captain! Nothing special to report. Combat patrol sighted in sector seventy-eight. Receiving you strength four. Medic! Enemy aircraft approaching left! Mother of God, please shoot me! Yes, Colonel! Gunshot fracture in right forearm. Fix . . . bayonets! Lunge, twist, withdraw! Watch out for snipers! I'm a soldier, I like being a soldier, the Führer was lucky to get me! Enemy breaking through on left flank, position under concentrated fire, delaying action in progress. Medic! QWW (Is reciprocal wave change possible?) Permission to pass through own lines? Yes, sir! Certainly, sir! At once, sir!

And now it was over, done with, finished. He hadn't grasped this, but it really was.

The war was letting its children go.

Quast learned to live again. This he found easy, because even the bleakest and most humdrum of days had at least one good thing to offer: nobody would try to shoot him, just as he would do violence to no one.

The nights were harder. That was when tank tracks churned overhead, when he heard the cross between a cry and a grunt as the Russian with the slit eyes lunged at him, when he saw the bayonet flash and the crimson droplets spatter his hands and jacket, when his rifle butt crunched into the other man's skull, smashing it like an eggshell.

Shadows flitted towards him like bats, preceded by little spurts of flame. He tried to raise his rifle but couldn't move, and then his dreams were rudely interrupted: 'Stop it! How do you expect me to sleep if you holler like that?' Switching on the bedside lamp with a tremulous hand, he would look down at the face on the pillow – a petulant stranger's face – and long to be alone, and sadly reflect how few women were capable of inducing the kind of oblivion he'd once hoped to find.

He dreaded breakfast and its coffee-sipping, toast-muching inquisition – 'What got into you last night? My, you're jumpy!' – because he knew he'd never be able to explain. Why bother to regale the women who shared his bed with anecdotes that held not the slightest interest for them? And in the morning, when the intimate stranger had departed for her office with a final look of utter incomprehension, never to return, he would fling the windows wide and strip the bed, stuff the sheets into the linen basket as though exorcizing his nocturnal phantoms, and remove every last trace of the female intruder whose physical nearness he had so fiercely craved only hours before.

But once in the years that followed, when haunted yet again by those ghosts from the past, he woke to feel a hand on his sweaty cheek. 'Don't worry,' said the woman beside him, 'I'm here.' And he turned and buried his face in her bed-warm breast. And he knew, as she drowsily stroked his head, that love alone could bring him deliverance.